The Parent's Handbook to Speech Therapy

Theory, Strategies, and Interactive
Exercises for
Enhancing Your Child's
Communication Skills

Richard Bass

2 FREE Bonuses!

Receive a FREE Planner for Kids and a copy of the Positive Discipline Playbook by scanning below!

Table of Contents

Introduction

Challenges are what makes life interesting and overcoming them is what makes life meaningful.
—Joshua Marine

There isn't a formula for parenting that can prepare moms and dads for the unique experience of raising children. Bringing a human being into this world is no easy feat, but soon after that comes other challenges like making sure your little human being can eat, sleep, play, and grow.

As a parent, you are a real-life superhero, that's for sure. However, you are not a magician. There are some early childhood developmental issues your child may experience that you cannot control. Acknowledging and accepting this fact is the first step to adapting to your child's developmental journey and providing the support and nurturing environment they need to mature at their own pace.

Have you ever felt guilty for your child's delayed speech and caught yourself thinking, "I have tried everything, but my kid refuses to talk?" You may feel responsible for ensuring that your child grows up in the same sequence as other children and think the inability to achieve that goal reflects your own shortcomings.

What you don't give yourself enough credit for is being a dedicated and loving parent—if you weren't, you wouldn't be drawn to reading this type of book. Nevertheless, even the most dedicated and loving parents cannot wave a wand and fill their children's mouths with words. The truth is that since no two children are the same, it is normal for some children to go through developmental milestones quicker or slower than other children.

So, take a deep breath and pinch yourself. You are doing the best that you can for your child. Delays in speech formation are more common than you think.

The U.S. Centers for Disease Control and Prevention found that approximately 1 in 6 children (or 17% of children in America) is living with at least one developmental delay (Cleveland Clinic, 2023). In other words, they are not reaching the standard developmental milestones (i.e., rolling over, waving their hands, or saying their first words) within the average time frame.

Children with speech and language delays take longer to communicate verbally and recognize or use language, but this shouldn't send you into a panic. Delayed speech is not denied speech and the dream of hearing your little one utter full sentences or articulate themselves clearly will come to pass. However, how and when this dream comes to pass is something that you cannot determine. Remember, this is your child's process, and the best you can do is provide a safe and stimulating environment for them to be encouraged to speak.

The Purpose of This Book

The purpose of this book is to educate parents with children aged 3-13 on speech delays and provide practical at-home interventions based on the principles of speech therapy. While the age-appropriate goals and strategies offered in this book may encourage children to speak, it is still recommended to seek a medical diagnosis and start professional treatment for speech problems immediately.

Parents reading this book may have some burning questions, such as:

- How can I find out whether my child is a late talker or living with an undiagnosed learning or mental health disorder?

- What goals, routines, and milestones can I set for my child to promote speech?

- What games and exercises can I play with my child to encourage them to speak?

- What type of home environment is most conducive to helping my child learn how to speak?

- What can I do if my child refuses to speak even after we have introduced him/her to different tools and exercises?

These and many more questions will be addressed through sound and practical wisdom shared by author and educator, Richard Bass, who has extensive knowledge and background on children's mental health, disabilities, and early childhood development.

Bass's hope for sharing the information provided in the following chapters is to help parents gain a better understanding of their children and be more supportive as they learn how to talk at their own pace and time. Parents will also walk away with tips on how to create a nurturing home environment that encourages learning (and making mistakes) and reduces stress and anxiety around communication.

A 30-to-60-minute session, once a week, with a speech pathologist is not enough practice for your child to start talking. Even though you cannot "speed up the process," you can reinforce principles of speech therapy through play-based learning in the safety and comfort of your home!

Chapter 1:

Raising Your Little Einstein

I can't change the direction of the wind, but I can adjust my sails to always reach my destination.
—Jimmy Dean

The Einstein Syndrome

As a parent, it is normal for you to start worrying when your child reaches the three-year milestone without having learned how to speak. While speech delays are common, you may fear that there could be other undiagnosed medical conditions in question, which could potentially prevent your child from speaking.

Albert Einstein's mother ran through the same type of worst-case scenario when her baby boy couldn't speak full sentences at the age of three. His speech only kicked in when he was five years old, and up until that point, there was little hope of him becoming fluent in speech.

Nevertheless, Einstein's speech delay didn't mean that other aspects of his development were delayed too. In fact, his mother and teachers discovered that little Einstein was highly developed (performed better than other children) in other areas, such as cognitive development. Many centuries later, the term "Einstein Syndrome" was coined by doctors who saw similar cases of children with speech delays but giftedness in other areas.

What is unique about Einstein Syndrome is that children with this condition learn to speak fluently later on and remain advanced in certain areas. For example, in his book *Late-Talking Children*, American economist Thomas Sowell highlights a few areas children with Einstein Syndrome are gifted (Sowell, 2008):

- short- and long-term memory
- analytical skills
- unique ability to use numbers
- concentration skills
- musical abilities

Often, speech and language delay is seen as a symptom of autism, however, many late-talking children aren't on the autism spectrum. When doctors cannot find traces of autism in children with delayed speech, they sometimes diagnose them with Einstein Syndrome.

The purpose of highlighting this particular condition is not to fill your head with more concerns and doubts, but rather to plant seeds of optimism. Albert Einstein only started talking in full sentences at the age of five, but his delayed speech didn't stop him from being successful later in life. Some may even argue that his speech delay was a sign of how gifted he was and that he was going to live an extraordinary life.

Take a few moments to shift your focus away from your child's speech delay and consider other developmental areas they are ahead in. For example, does your child have outstanding problem-solving skills? Do they demonstrate high empathy? Or do they have advanced fine and gross motor skills? Recognize the fact that your child's giftedness in other areas will remain with them for the rest of their life, whereas their speech issues can be corrected permanently within a few years.

What Are Developmental Milestones?

Developmental milestones are behaviors that children generally learn by a certain age. They serve as growth targets that parents and doctors use to assess whether young children are developing as expected. If not, they can quickly identify developmental delays.

It is important to understand that developmental delays are not indicators of serious conditions. It takes several years of screenings and assessments to diagnose children with co-occurring conditions. However, even when co-occurring conditions have been found, it is still possible for children to catch up on their development with the right support and treatment.

During your routine visits to the pediatrician's office, your child will be examined to determine which new milestones they have achieved. The doctor will also give you an indication of the age-appropriate behaviors your child should be able to carry out. It is also recommended for you to carry out tests and examinations at home to assess the pace of your child's growth.

The following chart provides speech and language milestones for your child aged three to six (CDC, 2018):

Age	Developmental milestone (speech and language)
3 years old	• sustains a conversation for at least two back-and-forth exchanges • asks simple who, what, where, how, and when questions • describes the action taking place in a picture book • responds with their first name when asked to • communicates well enough for parents, siblings, and close family to understand
4 years old	• talks in sentences with four or more words • recites words and phrases from nursery rhymes, stories, or songs

Age	Developmental milestone (speech and language)
	• describes at least one activity that occurred during the day
	• knows how to describe the purpose or function of an object
5 years old	• creates fictional stories or tells a story about a real past event
	• answers basic comprehension questions about a book or nursery rhyme after listening
	• sustains a conversation for more than three back-and-forth exchanges
	• recognizes and uses rhyming words
6 years old	• communicates well enough to be understood by a stranger
	• uses a range of grammatical skills, such as speaking in past tense, making sentences with plurals, and using possessive language.
	• asks questions and inquires about the meaning of words
	• tells stories and recounts a sequence of events in the correct order

Is It Normal for Your Child to Have Speech Delays?

Speech and language delays are the most common type of developmental delay, affecting one out of five young children. In many cases, your child doesn't need to seek treatment because their speech will naturally develop with time and extra support. However, if there are co-occurring conditions, like autism, ADHD, hearing loss, or learning problems, you may decide to seek a professional treatment plan from a medical doctor.

You can identify speech delays by taking note of common speech behaviors. For example, by the time your child reaches the two-year mark, they should be able to say 50 words. Keeping a log of your child's vocabulary is as simple as making a list on your phone of new words they can say. Before your child reaches the three-year mark, they should be able to string two words together and make simple phrases like, "Sit down," and "Thank you." By the age of three, your child's vocabulary should have increased to 200 words or more and they should be able to string together three-word phrases or sentences.

When your child's speech doesn't improve between ages two and three, they may have speech delays. Other signs of speech delays include not being able to articulate words clearly, pointing to objects instead of asking for them by name, learning new words but having trouble remembering them, and recognizing only a few words.

It is also worth examining whether your child has a speech or language issue or both. Even though we tend to speak of speech and language delays together (using the umbrella term "speech delays"), they refer to separate development issues. For example, a child with speech delays has trouble letting the right sounds out of their mouth to form fluent sentences. On the other hand, a child with language delays has trouble recognizing, memorizing, and using a variety of words. Since speech and language are closely related and both necessary for clear communication, they are often corrected by a medical doctor known as a speech-language pathologist (SLP) using similar interventions.

Lastly, it is worth noting that speech delays can show up differently for each child. Doctors have discovered three common types of speech delays noticeable in toddlers and young children, which include:

- **Delays in expressive language:** Commonly known as "late talkers," children with this type of speech delay exhibit age-appropriate social skills and understanding but difficulty using words. With a little encouragement, they can catch up and expand their vocabulary.

- **Delays in expressive language and receptive language:** This group of children has difficulty using words and understanding language. For example, they may not be able to follow simple instructions or react to words like "No." Nevertheless, they exhibit age-appropriate social skills. It is common for children with expressive and receptive language delays to be diagnosed with a language disorder by a qualified SLP.

- **Delays in more than one developmental area:** The last group of children exhibit speech and language delays but show signs of other learning and developmental disabilities. They may struggle to express themselves using words and follow basic instructions but also exhibit delayed social skills.

What's important to remember when you discover speech delays is that your parenting style is not to blame. It is common for parents to feel guilty about their children's developmental delays, thinking they didn't do enough to support their little ones. However, that isn't true. Children have unique personalities and perspectives, which make them drawn to certain things and not as interested in others.

For example, you might have an easy-going child who doesn't feel motivated to talk right now or an intellectual child who prefers to observe and analyze situations rather than participate in them. Placing your child in a play and learning-centered environment may just be the gentle nudge they need to start communicating more.

It Takes Two to Talk

Modeling healthy communication behaviors can be a great way to encourage your child to use their words and express thoughts and feelings. Instead of speaking about your child or in the presence of your child, take a different approach and speak directly to them. They may not be able to reciprocate just yet, but at least they are getting to hear different pitches and tones, new vocabulary, and appropriate facial expressions and body language.

Since you are modeling healthy communication behaviors, take a moment to reflect on your communication habits. Think about how frequently you talk at home, the range of your voice, and the variety of words used. Are you somebody who freely expresses what they are thinking or feeling? Or do you only speak when giving updates or instructions?

Another exercise to practice is imagining what your child sees and hears when you communicate. Record yourself sharing about how your day went and play back the recording to hear how you sound. Consider your tone of voice, length of sentences, number of words used, and whether you sounded engaging, bored, or indifferent. Reflect on how you can improve the way you deliver messages to spark interest in your child.

When communicating with your child, remember that you are talking with someone who doesn't have as much emotional intelligence as you; therefore, your approach must be based on compassion and understanding. For example, your child won't understand that your harsh tone of voice is due to the frustration of being stuck in peak-hour traffic and getting home to a dirty kitchen. They are more likely to think they are being punished.

Being harsh or yelling at a late talker can be interpreted as aggressive discipline, which creates a lot of stress and anxiety around talking. For instance, to avoid upsetting you further, your child may become very silent and non-communicative. Moreover, speaking to them in this manner teaches your child that aggression is an acceptable form of expression and may develop behavioral issues.

So, how should you be communicating with your child? The simple answer is in a way that encourages them to listen. A caring and friendly tone of voice will grab and hold your child's attention longer than a strict and controlling voice. Even when you are disciplining your child for unacceptable behavior, do so in a way that promotes curiosity and learning. Be firm but compassionate in your delivery and go the extra mile to explain why the behavior is unacceptable and how they can correct their mistake next time.

Your child is also more likely to listen and learn when they have developed a trusting relationship with you. As such, it is important to spend quality time with your child in different social settings so they can observe how you interact and communicate with others. Focus on being open and enthusiastic in how you communicate in social contexts. This will cause your child to feel safe practicing how to speak around you because they trust you will display the same openness and enthusiasm with them.

If the idea of being a better communicator for your child gets you excited, then you will have plenty of parent-child communication strategies offered later in the book. There are also fun and interactive activities perfect to carry out at home, so you can encourage your little one to get talking!

Key Takeaway

One out of five children will experience speech delays and naturally learn how to communicate fluently over time, with extra support. Referring to developmental milestones can help you identify speech delays early but remember that these milestones are only guidelines and not rules for how your child should be growing. Treatment for speech delays is generally not required unless doctors suspect there may be co-occurring disorders that are affecting your child's ability to communicate effectively. But with that said, speech therapy and at-home speech exercises can be just what your child needs to feel motivated to talk!

Chapter 2:

Developmental Delay or

Developmental Disorder?

We all have a voice, but some of us need a little help finding it. —
Unknown

Delay vs. Disorder

It can be confusing to distinguish between developmental delays and disorders since these terms are often used interchangeably. Developmental delays occur when your child doesn't reach an expected milestone within a certain age. In other words, their growth is running behind schedule. As mentioned in the previous chapter, delays are common and nothing you should worry about because your child will naturally catch up with time.

Doctors and researchers are still unable to pinpoint what exactly causes many developmental delays, however, some attribute them to slow development. In general, these delays are short-term and don't require medical treatment, except when they are a symptom of underlying cognitive disabilities.

For your child to be diagnosed with a developmental disorder, they must show signs of mental or physical disabilities, or both, that affect their ability to perform daily functions such as learning, moving, playing, or communicating. These disabilities may show up anytime from birth until 22-years-old. This means that not all disabilities will appear during the early years of your child's life; some might be triggered by environmental factors or trauma experienced well into their childhood years. However, the earlier the developmental disorder is detected, the sooner you can start treatment.

The reason why it is crucial to distinguish between developmental delays and disorders is because the way you respond to them will differ. For example, speech and language delays do not require treatment, but when going that route, you can choose between indirect and direct interventions. Indirect interventions involve practicing speech exercises with your child and creating a learning-conducive environment at home.

Direct interventions involve seeking the help of an SLP, who can create a specific treatment plan to help your child with challenges they may have.

On the other hand, treating speech and language disorders requires a diagnosis from an SLP, followed by speech therapy and other types of therapy (i.e., occupational therapy, ABA therapy, etc.) to manage co-occurring conditions.

The Path Toward Getting Diagnosed

When you have concerns about your child's delayed speech, the first step is to schedule an assessment with a pediatrician. One of the first things a pediatrician will examine is your child's ability to react to sounds to rule out hearing loss. Once that has been checked and ruled out, they may examine the tongue and palate to see how they move together.

The pediatrician will share their findings and offer recommendations. One of their recommendations could be to complete further assessments with specialist doctors like an audiologist, neurologist, or speech and language pathologist (SLP).

If your child is suspected to have a speech and language disorder, they will be referred to an SLP, who specializes in treating various speech and language conditions. The SLP will conduct further assessments and determine what specific issues your child is experiencing. They can also determine whether speech or language issues are caused by language differences rather than a medical condition.

It is common for children living in bilingual households to have trouble recognizing and using different parts of speech or pronouncing and remembering words. Becoming fluent in two or more languages is a difficult task that requires a lot of practice. Thus, SLPs may refer children with this specific problem to specialists who understand the development of language skills in more than one language.

Treatment options for speech and language disorders are few but effective. The main treatment option is speech and language therapy (shortened to speech therapy), which seeks to correct speech delays. Some speech impediments, such as tongue-tie and cleft palate, require surgery to correct.

Besides speech therapy, a SLP may recommend early intervention services before your child starts school. Research has shown that speech delays in young children aged three to five can lead to difficulties with reading when they reach elementary school (McLaughlin, 2011). Getting extra support can significantly improve your child's performance at school and help them overcome some of the speech or language challenges they are experiencing.

With an SLP's referral, you may be able to access local early intervention services based on your child's needs. Many of these services provide state-funded programs, while some programs are offered at a reduced cost.

Causes of Speech Delays

A few years ago, dedicated mom, Katie Cloyd shared a story about her son Walker's journey toward diagnosing his speech issues (Cloyd, 2020). She had noticed for a while that he wasn't reaching the expected speech and language milestones like other children. However, the milestone gap only became significantly wider at two and a half years old.

His pediatrician recommended seeing an SLP, who later diagnosed Walker with receptive and expressive speech delays. The SLP encouraged them to start speech therapy immediately since Walker had become less responsive to language.

Speech therapy helped the little boy feel confident to speak again. One of the first milestones he achieved was being able to ask for snacks or go to the bathroom. Six months into speech therapy, before reaching his third birthday, Walker received another unexpected diagnosis.

Doctors found that on top of receptive and expressive speech delays, he was living with autism spectrum disorder (ASD) but showed no severe symptoms like cognitive impairments. The main area of focus was speech and language development.

There are many children like Walker whose speech delays are caused by underlying physical or developmental problems. In other words, it is not just a matter of slow growth, but a cognitive or behavioral issue that is causing the delays. Apart from slow development, consider the following common causes of speech delays:

Oral-Motor Problems

When a child experiences brain injuries or impairments, particularly in the areas of the brain that control speech, they may struggle to understand or use sounds and language. For example, a medical condition known as apraxia affects the brain's ability to send signals to the facial muscles. As a result, a child diagnosed with this condition may have difficulty moving their mouth to form speech.

Autism

It is common for a child diagnosed with a speech disorder to later get an autism diagnosis (or vice versa). This happens because speech delays are one of the symptoms of Autism. A medical study found that about half of children diagnosed between the ages of three and four hadn't reached the speech and language milestones for their age (Think, n.d.). Moreover, children with autism may display language problems like repeating the same words and phrases or not being able to read nonverbal communication.

Hearing Problems

Speech delays can also be caused by hearing problems. For example, a child diagnosed with auditory processing disorder may have a difficult time hearing sounds and words, which subsequently affects their speaking abilities.

Cognitive Disabilities

A child with cognitive disabilities that cause brain damage or impairments to vital parts of the brain may experience several developmental problems, including speech delays. Some of the speech and language challenges they may display include the inability to pronounce certain sounds, construct sentences, understand the meaning of words, produce sounds and words, or follow instructions.

It can be a great relief to discover the underlying cause of your child's speech delays because it means you can start treating all of the co-occurring conditions immediately. The earlier you start treatment, the quicker your child's speech and language skills can improve.

Types of Speech Disorders

There are several types of speech disorders recognized in the medical community. While each one describes a specific speech impediment, all of them make it difficult for children to create or form speech sounds required to build sentences and communicate with others.

Below is a detailed look into four common types of speech disorders:

Articulation Disorder

Articulation disorder refers to the inability to make certain sounds. For example, they might pronounce the "R" sound as an "L" sound or pronounce the "TH" sound as a "F" sound. The good news is that this speech error is not related to any mouth, ear, or brain conditions and can be corrected with speech therapy.

The main challenge a child with articulation disorder has is being able to move their lips, tongue, teeth, and palate in a way that produces different sounds. It can sometimes be tough to make out what words they are communicating because of the distorted speech sounds.

Common signs of articulation disorder include:

- Adding sounds or syllables onto words that shouldn't be there. For example, instead of saying "grass," the child might say "guh-rass."

- Mispronunciation of sounds, which at times may sound like a lisp. For example, instead of saying "wrong," the child might pronounce it as "long."

- Leaving out sounds or syllables when pronouncing words. For example, the child might omit the "B" in "ball" or the "D" in "food."

Articulation disorder affects a child's ability to socialize effectively. Elementary and middle school children living with this condition may become self-conscious about speaking or reading in public or show frustration when their speech is corrected. Going to therapy can boost their self-confidence and make them less fearful of social settings.

Phonological Disorder

Phonological disorder refers to the difficulty of combining sounds and syllables and pronouncing them correctly. For example, a child may be able to pronounce the "BA" sound, but when asked to say the word "baba," they respond with "dada."

Due to the many speech sound errors made, it can be challenging to understand what the child is communicating. In a classroom environment, they may have trouble with listening, reading, and writing.

Common signs of phonological disorder include:

- Pronouncing only one syllable in a word and leaving out the rest. For example, instead of saying "widow," the child might say "dow."

- Simplifying the pronunciation of a word by repeating one syllable. For example, the child might say "mama" instead of "Mason."

- Omitting a consonant sound from a word. For example, instead of saying the word "table," the child might say "able."

The examples mentioned above are known as phonological processes. When children are learning to speak, practicing these phonological processes is helpful. However, as they grow and get exposed to more skills, they must be encouraged to pronounce words in full.

In speech therapy, children who make these sound errors are taught the correct speech and sound rules so they can construct words properly. Exercises taught to them by an SLP will include an element of listening, as this is an important step in learning how to clearly articulate words.

Disfluency Disorder

Disfluency refers to irregularities that occur while communicating information, such as stuttering, jumping from one idea to the next, or the difficulty of expressing ideas simply and clearly.

Children with disfluency disorder often rush to speak before they pause and think about what they want to say. Some may even get distracted or confused while attempting to express an idea because their thoughts are running faster than they can catch up.

Some of the common signs of disfluency include:

- Repeating whole words or syllables while speaking. For example, the child might say "I want-want to play outside," or "C-c-can you help me?"

- Adding filler words like "uh" or "um" in a sentence. For example, the child might say, "I think, uh, it will be cold, uh, tomorrow."

- Revising sentences while speaking. For example, the child might say, "Can we, no, can I go to the park?"

Another form of disfluency is stuttering. Children who stutter tend to repeat syllables or words stretch words and create a longer sound. Stuttering causes a lot of frustration for children, which may lead to avoiding speaking with long sentences, reading passages in class, asking questions, or having impromptu conversations with others.

Even though stuttering is a type of disfluency, it is typically caused by genetic or environmental factors, not delayed speech development. Neurological disorders like ADHD, autism, or Tourette syndrome can co-occur with stuttering. Nonetheless, the most common treatment for stuttering is speech therapy.

Voice Disorder

A voice disorder is a common type of speech disorder detectable in young children. It is characterized by a difference in the sound, pitch, and resonance of the child's voice compared to other children their age.

For example, they might have a soft and inaudible voice or a hoarse and loud voice. Depending on what specific voice issues they have, they are prone to getting tired quickly when speaking (i.e., losing their breath) or having difficulty projecting their voice so others can hear them.

Signs and symptoms of a voice disorder show up during infancy. Children with weak cries, hoarse voices, or noisy breathing may need to see a SLP for professional assessments and diagnosis. Voice disorders are treated with speech therapy and various voice exercises. Only 5% of children diagnosed with voice disorders live with the condition permanently (RCH, 2018). This means that within a few years, your child's voice problems will clear up on their own.

Types of Language Disorders

Language disorders are referred to by some therapists and doctors as "speech disorders." However, a distinction needs to be made since language disorders present specific language-related delays and challenges.

When a child is diagnosed with a language disorder, they normally have difficulty understanding words and commands or expressing what they think or feel. Doctors classify language disorders under two broad categories. The first is receptive language disorder, which describes the inability to hear or read language. Some children may have severe hearing and reading problems that require surgery while others have moderate hearing and reading problems that can be treated with speech therapy.

Symptoms of receptive language disorder include the inability to:

- understand what people are saying
- learn new words
- follow instructions
- understand what is read

- pick up on nonverbal communication

The second category is expressive language disorder. Children with this type of condition struggle with spoken communication and may display tendencies like mumbling words, stuttering, and going silent due to not knowing how to respond.

Symptoms of expressive language disorder include the inability to:

- use words properly
- sing songs or read out loud
- express thoughts and feelings
- name or describe objects
- use gestures or other forms of nonverbal communication

It is common for doctors to diagnose children with both disorders at the same time because of how closely related these conditions are to each other. Co-occurring disorders that are sometimes diagnosed alongside language disorders are autism, brain tumors, down syndrome, or cerebral palsy.

Moreover, language delays or challenges can be extremely frustrating for young children, who desire to express themselves but have difficulties doing so. As a result, children with language disorders may perform poorly at school, get into trouble frequently with their parents and schoolteachers, and have an increased risk of developing behavioral issues. Therefore, it is important to seek a diagnosis for language problems as early as possible to start with treatment.

What Happens After the Diagnosis?

Getting a diagnosis is a huge step in your child's recovery. Your expert doctor will complete a thorough examination and create a treatment plan to address specific speech and language problems. However, this is where the real work starts. Alongside the SLP, you will need to step in and provide the necessary support and reinforcement at home.

Children with speech delays require consistent practice to learn and remember various speech and language skills. One- or two-hour sessions with the SLP per week are not nearly enough practice for your child to improve their speaking abilities. They rely on your input and participation to memorize and practice what may come easily to other children.

Your SLP will provide your child with the tools to communicate effectively. It is your responsibility as their parent to remind your child of how to use the tools in different social settings. Since you are with your child more often than the therapist, your involvement in the process is incredibly important.

Instead of seeing this as a lot of pressure on your shoulders, think of it as a unique opportunity to strengthen the bond you have with your child. The time you spend together will be filled with play and learning, and some of your child's core childhood memories will be based on your loving interactions.

With that said, there are a few strategies you can practice to prepare yourself for this significant role in your child's treatment:

1. Learn about the various speech milestones

While speech milestones may not apply to every child, they set the benchmark for the progress your child should be making with their speaking abilities. Look at different speech milestones charts (as charts can vary on what they include or exclude) and familiarize yourself with where they are expected to be compared to other children. This information can be helpful when visiting a specialist and seeking further medical assessments down the line.

2. Find support through therapy

It is always recommended to speak to your pediatrician whenever you have concerns or questions about your child's speech or language skills. Don't hold onto your worries when you can easily clear them up with a doctor. A pediatrician may or may not refer you to a specialist doctor for more assessments. However, if they do, the advantage is that you get to start treatment sooner rather than later.

3. Share the journey with friends, family, and community members

Due to how stressful speech problems can be for both you and your child, it can be a great relief to have a close circle of friends, family, and community members (i.e., school teachers, therapists, nurses, etc.), who can offer advice, provide emotional support, and look out for your best interests. Your community support may include physical or virtual parent groups and forums where you get to share your experiences with people who are going through (or have been through) the same journey.

What's worth emphasizing is that you are not alone on this journey. There are plenty of resources and professionals available to answer your questions and offer tools that can encourage your child to speak. It simply takes making the first contact to build your tribe of supporters and get the help your child needs!

Key Takeaway

There is a striking difference between a speech delay and a disorder. A speech delay is a normal part of growing up that often corrects itself without seeking treatment. On the other hand, a speech disorder interferes with your child's daily function and requires treatment through speech therapy or early intervention services to address. To assess whether your child is living with a speech disorder, consult with a pediatrician and go through the necessary steps. Don't be dismayed if you discover a speech disorder. There are plenty of resources and support available to you and your child to make this journey of recovery smooth and enjoyable!

Chapter 3:

Everything You Need to Know

About Speech Therapy

Speech therapy is an art that deserves to be more widely known. You cannot imagine the acrobatics your tongue mechanically performs this treatment aims to produce all the sounds of a language.
—Jean-Dominique Bauby

What Is Speech Therapy?

One of the most common treatments for speech delays and disorders is speech and language therapy or simply speech therapy for short. This treatment aims to gradually improve your child's speaking abilities by teaching them new skills. Through ongoing practice and repetition, your child can recognize and memorize words, sounds, and various speech and language rules.

Taking your child for speech therapy is a decision you won't regret, even if your child has normal speech delays and doesn't need speech therapy. They can still benefit from attending regular sessions and walk away with the following skills:

- early language skills

- voice range, control, and resonance

- understanding new words and language

- comfortable use of language

- clear articulation of sounds and words

The type of speech therapy treatment offered to your child will depend on their age, medical history, and specific speech or language challenges they might have. There are numerous interventions your therapist can recommend to your child, but quality is better than quantity when it comes to treating speech issues. However, even with numerous interventions, the approach to speech therapy is the same—integrating play with learning.

Who Is a Speech Therapist?

We have briefly touched on the question about the type of specialist doctor who performs speech therapy. These special doctors are referred to as speech-language pathologists, sometimes called "speech therapists." They are educated in the fields of human development, communication, and disorders, and have, at least, a master's degree.

To start practicing speech therapy, SLPs will obtain a licensure in the field, as well as a certificate of clinical competency from a regulatory body called the "American Speech-Language-Hearing Association" (ASHA). When shopping around for your speech therapist, ensure they are recognized and certified by ASHA, as this is a good indication that they are following the right processes. ASHA-certified SLPs need to pass a national exam and complete a supervised clinical fellowship before they can get accredited.

SLPs work mostly with children on a one-on-one basis. They operate in a learning-conducive and child-friendly office or classroom. Depending on your child's needs, the SLP may recommend group sessions with other children or sessions where you practice exercises with your child.

We have mentioned that SLPs have a toolbox full of interventions to correct speech issues. However, not every intervention will necessarily work to address your child's issues. The initial assessment that your child completes with the SLP will help them determine what kind of intervention would be most effective for your child. There are three interventions the SLP may offer:

1. **Language intervention activities**

For a child with difficulty recognizing and pronouncing different words, the SLP may focus on expanding their vocabulary and modeling the correct way to pronounce words. This is done through interactive activities like reading picture books, singing nursery rhymes, or talking about objects and events.

2. **Articulation therapy**

For a child who has difficulty producing the correct sounds or expressing themselves clearly, the SLP may engage in repetitive back-and-forth conversation where the child gets to practice repeating sounds, syllables, words, and sentences during play activities. The SLP may also help the child recognize certain sounds in text and make the correct tongue, teeth, and palate movements to say them properly.

3. Oral-motor/feeding and swallowing therapy

For a child with weak lip, tongue, or jaw muscles that make it difficult for them to eat or swallow food properly, the SLP will introduce a variety of oral exercises that target those specific muscle groups. To enhance oral awareness during chewing and swallowing food, the SLP may also introduce the child to different flavors, textures, and temperatures.

While speech therapy is optional for a child with speech delays, it is not optional for a child with a speech or language disorder. Other developmental disorders may also require your child to attend speech therapy. Some of these include:

- Autism spectrum disorder (ASD)

- motor planning problems

- weak oral muscles

- hearing impairments

- cognitive development delays

- cleft palate

- chronic hoarseness

- traumatic brain injury

- feeding and swallowing disorders

- respiratory problems (i.e., breathing disorders)

Research shows that children who start speech therapy before the age of five tend to see better results than those who start later. This doesn't mean that speech therapy won't be effective on older children and preteens. They will simply take longer to unlearn existing speech patterns and develop new ones.

The best way to find an SLP is to seek a referral from your pediatrician. Alternatively, you can search for qualified SLPs on medical online directories or browse on ASHA's website. Remember to check if your child's SLP is licensed to practice in your state and has experience treating children who have similar speech impairments as your child.

What Happens During Speech Therapy?

Speech therapy for children seeks to teach and reinforce speech and language skills through interactive play. In most cases, children aren't even aware they are developing skills because the learning occurs through fun activities that don't feel strenuous.

For older children and preteens, speech therapy may focus on strengthening or rebuilding particular skills. This can be challenging (hence it may take longer) since it requires replacing patterns already formed in the brain with new or improved ones.

On the first day of speech therapy, the SLP will set speech or language goals and strategies to achieve within a certain time frame. Sessions are structured around these goals and strategies and progress is monitored and reviewed continuously. During treatment, the SLP may identify additional problem areas to work on that present challenges for your child. The true test of whether or not treatment is working for your child is observing their behaviors, engaging in conversations with them, and practicing speech therapy exercises at home.

Speech therapy will continue for as long as you are happy with the results and desire your child to get constant practice. However, a child with normal speech delays won't need speech therapy for as long as a child with a severe speech disorder. Age is another factor to consider when thinking about the duration of treatment. Typically, the earlier you start, the sooner you can quit therapy.

Does Speech Therapy Work?

As a parent who is willing to invest money into getting the best treatment for your child, you may want assurance that speech therapy works.

Before evaluating the success rate of speech therapy, the first thing to note is that every child will respond to speech therapy differently. Some may be quick to grasp and memorize the skills while others may take a little longer. Nevertheless, this doesn't make the treatment any less effective.

A study observed 730 children (up to the age of 16) who were diagnosed with speech and language impediments and referred to the Paediatric Speech and Language Therapy Service of Middlesbrough Primary Care Trust between January 1999 and April 2000 (Broomfield & Dodd, 2011).

Some children were offered speech therapy and others were not. The findings showed that an average of six hours of speech therapy in six months can significantly improve speech and language performance. Furthermore, receiving speech therapy treatment was seen to be more advantageous for children with speech and language impediments than not receiving treatment at all.

In general, speech therapy is known to have a high success rate and help children achieve visible improvements in speech and language skills. However, some factors can influence each child's success rate, which include:

- **Age:** It is recommended for a child to start speech therapy before they turn five years old to achieve the best results.

- **Severity:** Simple cases of speech delays are easier to treat than severe cases of speech and language disorders that require a much longer and complex treatment plan.

- **Commitment:** Consistent and frequent speech therapy sessions yield better results overall. Practice should also continue at home through exercises to reinforce the skills learned.

- **Medical history:** If there are other co-occurring medical conditions or disorders, speech therapy may be one of many interventions used to treat development issues. As a result, the time it takes to improve speech and language may be longer.

- **Support:** Having a supportive network of friends, family, doctors, and schoolteachers can provide easy access to information and help to reinforce speech and language skills in different aspects of the child's life.

When starting speech therapy, go in with an open and curious mind. Focus on learning as much as you can from your SLP so that you can practice the same skills and techniques used in therapy at home. Depending on your child's particular needs, they may come out of therapy cured of their speech issues. But at the very least, expect them to communicate better and display more confidence talking.

Six ABA Principles Used in Speech Therapy

Applied Behavioral Analysis (ABA) is a therapy that focuses on understanding and correcting human behavior. It is commonly used to treat developmental disorders and learning disabilities and can be modified for people of all ages. According to ABA therapists, human behavior can be broken down into three components:

- Antecedent: Behavior is triggered by a cue or stimulus that prompts a reaction.

- Behavior: Following the cue or stimulus, the actual behavior is carried down.

- Consequence: For every input, there must be an equivalent output. Behaviors, both acceptable and unacceptable, lead to specific outcomes.

The goal of ABA is to help patients, including children, desire positive behaviors. To do this, the therapist must identify and seek to understand the cause of the unwanted behavior and follow this by reinforcing desired behaviors with strategies like offering rewards.

ABA therapy is sometimes used by SLPs to treat children with speech and language problems and help them correct and reinforce positive communication skills. There are similarities between ABA and speech therapy, such as they both seek to equip children with tools to live an autonomous and successful life outside of therapy.

Additionally, they both use positive reinforcement to encourage children to engage in desired behaviors. The difference between them, however, is that ABA uses a set of behavioral techniques to develop any kind of behavioral or learning skill whereas speech therapy uses a wide range of strategies to improve specifically speech and language skills. Nevertheless, some ABA principles are effective in helping children build receptive and expressive speech and language skills.

In this section, we will explore six ABA principles that SLPs and parents can practice with children. If you are looking for new approaches to speech and language training, then you may find these six principles to be refreshing and exciting. Bear in mind that speech and language training can take place beyond the therapy room and home. Every outing that you take with your child, whether it be to the grocery store or park, is a perfect opportunity to practice the following principles.

Pairing

A child must have a desire to learn to be receptive to new ideas and skills. This desire is partly determined by their relationship with the teacher, in this case, their SLP or parent. Pairing is the process of building and nurturing a strong relationship with your child so that they desire to play and learn with you. The better paired you are with your child, the less resistance they will put up when you ask them questions or give instructions.

Since many speech exercises require back-and-forth conversations or repetition, it is important to have a tight bond with your child so that you can pick up on their moods, attention level, non-verbal language, and when they need a break. You will also be able to quickly pick up on activities they like or dislike and the best approach to learning to keep the environment relaxed and encouraging.

Tip: Take 10 minutes each day to engage in unstructured play with your child. Choose age-appropriate games that allow both of you to engage with one another and solve problems or unleash your creativity.

Positive Reinforcement

Positive reinforcement is a popular ABA principle that has been used in other forms of therapy like speech therapy. Positive reinforcement aims to reward desired behaviors and ignore or remove your attention from undesirable behaviors. For example, whenever your child pronounces a word correctly, you respond with enthusiasm and a high-five. When they mispronounce the same word, you simply repeat the word with an emotionless expression until they get it right (or come very close to getting it right).

This principle is a move away from harsh discipline when children make mistakes, which has the potential to hurt rather than help children. Instead of making them feel bad about the errors they have made, positive reinforcement encourages you to celebrate the moments when they succeed. This can lead to less fear of making mistakes during speech and language training and heightened feelings of confidence.

What makes positive reinforcement effective is when you reward your child with what they are more receptive to. For example, if your child enjoys physical touch, giving them a hug or high-five can be encouraging. However, if they do not enjoy physical touch, the same behavior can be received negatively. Find out what type of rewards your child enjoys and create opportunities to reward them for their efforts.

Tip: Identify three positive reinforcements that you can alternate during speech and language training. Remember to choose behaviors that your child finds rewarding.

Negative Reinforcement

Negative reinforcement refers to taking things away to encourage your child to use language. The purpose of this ABA principle is to help your child switch from relying solely on non-verbal communication to verbalizing their needs. This is effective for late talkers who may be too comfortable with pointing or crying to express what they want.

For example, before handing a ball over to your child, wait a few seconds for them to say the phrase, "Please may I have the ball?" before giving it to them. If your child has a particular food they dislike, you might encourage them to say the phrase, "I don't want it," before removing the item from their plate. A negative reinforcement sequence is always followed by a reward (i.e., positive reinforcement) to remind your child of the desirable behavior.

Tip: Make a list of phrases that you would like your child to learn and a few scenarios that might prompt them to use those phrases. Practice negative reinforcement to motivate your child to use their words.

Task Analysis

When introducing children to new skills, ABA therapists break them down into smaller tasks or activities and have them complete each one, step-by-step. It is, therefore, not obvious to children that they are practicing a specific skill because it is presented as fun games or activities. As time goes on, children are expected to play the games or activities with less assistance. Eventually, they will be able to play the games or activities with no assistance at all, which is a sign that they are proficient in that specific area.

Tip: Write down a speech or language skill that you would like to teach your child. Beneath the skill, identify five smaller tasks or activities that can reinforce the skill. Include simple instructions to complete the tasks or activities.

Prompting/Prompt Fading

Prompting is the act of helping your child practice new skills by offering guidance. This may be in the form of mouth movements, hand gestures, demonstrations, instructions, or offering the first sound or word to jog their memory. At the beginning of speech and language training, your child will need assistance to recognize and use different speech rules. Offering prompts can make the process of remembering information challenging yet fun at the same time.

After a while, you can practice what is known as prompt fading, which is the act of gradually removing prompts until your child can practice skills independently. It is important to never rush the process of removing prompts because they can be a great source of encouragement for your child. You will know when your child doesn't need as many prompts by the speed of their responses when you provide a cue.

Tip: For each speech or language exercise, write down at least one prompt that you can use to make the exercise memorable for your child.

Shaping

Shaping is the process of leading your child toward the desired outcome through repetition and positive reinforcement. Before you can "shape" your child, you need to identify the desired goal and steps on how you will reach it. For example, you may want to teach your child how to say "Apple" instead of

"Papple." The first step may be to practice the first syllable "Ah" several times and provide rewards after every successful try. The second step may be to practice the second syllable "Puhl" several times, followed by rewards. Gradually, this process helps your child learn how to pronounce the word correctly. Apple!

These six ABA principles can be practiced whenever you identify a learning opportunity. For example, if you are planning to go to the grocery store with your child, you might say, "We are going to the grocery store. Where are we going?" This prompt would trigger them to respond with "grocery store." To reward them for answering correctly you can smile and say, "That's right. Well done!" The versatility of these principles makes them perfect to reinforce speech and language skills for any occasion.

Key Takeaway

Speech and language therapy, better known as speech therapy, is an effective treatment to address speech delays and disorders. It is administered by a speech therapist who is formerly called a speech-language pathologist (SLP). They are trained to assess, diagnose, and offer interventions to correct speech and language impediments. The type of interventions offered to your child will depend on their age, needs, and medical history. Speech therapy has a high success rate and can be practiced by children of any age. However, the sooner your child starts therapy, the quicker you will see results.

Chapter 4:

What Does "Play" Have to Do

With It?

The activities that are the easiest, cheapest, and most fun to do—such as singing, playing games, reading, storytelling, and just talking and listening—are also the best for child development.
—Jerome Singer

How Play Supports Early Childhood Development

In the previous chapter, we explored speech therapy as a treatment option for speech delays and disorders. We found that it was the most commonly used treatment for speech and language problems, and with such a high success rate, there is no doubt that your child will benefit from taking sessions of speech therapy than not doing so at all.

We are now preparing to move away from broad discussions about speech therapy and focus on how you, as a parent, can incorporate aspects of this therapy at home. While this book seeks to raise awareness about treatment options for speech delays, the main goal is to empower you to take a proactive approach to your child's growth and development.

Toward the end of the book, you will be given a list of different speech and language exercises to practice with your child. However, before you can start browsing through the exercises, it is important to understand how to administer speech therapy at home. In this chapter, we will look at the significance of play in developing speech and language skills, so you can motivate your child to learn.

What is the first image or thought that crosses your mind when you think of play? Do you see an image of your child kneeling on the floor and playing with his or her toys? Or perhaps the trails of dirt left on the floor or flickers of paint on the wall in the aftermath of a fun-filled day?

All of this action, and more, occurs when your child is playing. However, what you may not always see is the learning process taking place in the background. Play is an activity that teaches your child valuable developmental skills in an enjoyable and stress-free environment.

Different games and activities show your child how to move and control their body, socialize with others, solve problems, make informed decisions, and practice desirable behaviors. Your child may not realize it, but their brain is hard at work whenever they are engaged in play.

The common misconception about play is that at some stage, your child will outgrow it. The truth is that there is no age limit when it comes to exploring, tapping into your imagination, and exercising different cognitive muscles. Even grown adults engage in play through age-appropriate activities like reading, meditation, coffee dates with friends, or traveling.

The good news is that you don't need to persuade young children to play. They have a natural curiosity that leads to experimentation and creative work. Play also brings an immense amount of pleasure to young children, which makes the learning and problem-solving aspect of the activity feel rewarding.

Below are some examples of how play enhances early childhood development:

- **Play and physical development:** Active play encourages your child to move different muscle groups, practice coordination and balance, and maintain good physical well-being.

- **Play and social development:** Imaginative play, like role-playing or dressing up, can teach your child appropriate social cues and expectations and reinforce positive values. Playing in groups reinforces emotional skills like self-control, sharing, negotiation, and empathy.

- **Play and cognitive development:** Both individual and group play enhance your child's cognitive skills, such as increasing their ability to memorize information, think in a logical sequence, solve problems, and maintain focus.

- **Play and literacy development:** Through play, your child can expand their vocabulary, practice listening and speaking skills, learn how to tell stories, and practice writing skills by doodling or painting.

Experts reveal that sedentary activities like watching TV can hamper your child's physical, mental, and social development (WHO, 2019). Thus, less time should be spent on the couch and more time should be spent engaging in age-appropriate play. So, with that said, how many hours a day does your child spend playing?

Consider the following guidelines provided by the World Health Organization for children aged 3-4 (WHO, 2019):

- 180 minutes spent on a variety of physical activities (60 minutes should be dedicated to moderate-to-rigorous physical activity).

- Encouraged to move after sitting down for an hour (when traveling, let your child out of the pram or car seat after an hour for a quick break).

- Limit screen time to one hour or less per day.

- Encourage 10-13 hours of good-quality sleep (including naps during the day).

What Is a Play-Based Approach to Learning?

Introducing new concepts and skills through play is known as play-based learning. It is an approach used by therapists, teachers, and early childhood care services to make learning enjoyable, interactive, and unstructured. Instead of going the traditional route and presenting a lot of information that the child needs to process, skills are taught through trial and error, problem-solving, asking questions, and creative thinking.

In the classroom or therapy room, play-based learning can take place in the following ways:

- allowing children to engage with resources like flipping through picture books on their own or manipulating an object (e.g., making different shapes using playdough).

- creating personalized play experiences based on the child's interests, abilities, and developmental needs.

- observing how a child plays to evaluate developmental strengths and weaknesses and modify play experiences to improve areas where they might be delayed.

- sharing play experiences with a child by talking to them, solving problems together, and role-playing positive behaviors.

- providing sufficient blocks of time for a child to play without being interrupted. This free time allows for a child's ideas to naturally develop and creative thinking to take place in a stress-free environment.

As you can tell, play-based learning takes your child through the process of getting to answers instead of presenting the answers upfront and asking your child to memorize them. From the time they start playing, their brains are actively working to recognize, categorize, process, and interpret information.

If you are interested in adopting a play-based approach to learning at home, remember to include the following elements in your activities:

1. Self-direction

Allow your child to decide what games or activities to play and how to carry out the tasks. Be open to modifying the time spent playing based on their interest levels. Moreover, even when the activity requires a second person or group of people, give your child a few minutes to make sense of the activity on their own. Be there to supervise your child but let them take the lead.

2. Unstructured experience

Many games and activities come with rules. However, how the rules are interpreted should be left to your child. For example, instead of using pencils to draw a picture, your child may want to use paint and a paintbrush. It is also important to give your child space to make mistakes and correct themselves without your direction. If they are performing the task incorrectly, resist the urge to direct them. Play is about exploring the possibilities of what something might be, rather than being committed to a single outcome.

3. **Process-oriented**

Focus on being in the moment and enjoying the process of discovery and adventure. Whether or not your child achieves the aims of the game or activity doesn't matter as much as how much they enjoyed the process. Learning doesn't occur at the end once the goal has been accomplished; it occurs in the middle during experimentation.

4. **Fun**

Keep learning fun by introducing age-appropriate games or activities that are not too complicated to carry out and provide plenty of opportunities for your child to participate. It may help to learn which type of games or activities your child enjoys and incorporate these into your learning material.

Play-based learning at home reinforces developmental skills while giving your child the freedom to express themselves in whichever way they choose. Your child is still learning, but now they are doing so without the pressure that often comes with it.

The Role of Play in Speech Therapy

Play-based speech therapy uses play as the main tool to engage children and introduce speech and language skills. Depending on the child's age, the therapist will use toys, objects, games, or activities to encourage them to talk. Play can also be used in role-playing to model desirable communication behaviors.

Play is critical when teaching preschoolers speech and language skills. This is because there are several other developmental benefits they get from engaging in playful experiences, such as:

- Play reduces the stress and anxiety around learning, which enables young children to absorb information in a low-stakes atmosphere and take risks without being afraid to make mistakes.

- Play enhances young children's social skills and helps them practice appropriate social behaviors and how to regulate their emotions.

- Play is an effective tool for developing language skills and expanding young children's vocabularies, grammar, and storytelling abilities.

For older children and preteens, telepractice play-based speech therapy provides an age-appropriate and stimulating approach to learning. Due to their level of maturity and independence, they may not be interested in playing with toys like smaller children. Thus, online interactive speech therapy games can be a great alternative for them.

The combination of technology and gamification to earn rewards keeps older children motivated to learn. Furthermore, many of these online games stimulate the senses by providing high-quality video content, and images. Children are transported into a virtual world that promises to keep them entertained while offering plenty of speech and language practice.

Another benefit of telepractice play-based therapy is the variety of games and exercises offered. They provide parents and children with a range of options to choose from based on specific learning goals and needs. The entire learning experience can be personalized to suit each child's interests, skill level, and preferences.

Online speech therapy games also tend to feel more rewarding than physical games. For example, gamification features may include hearing a bell when an answer is correct, receiving badges or medals for reaching milestones, and being able to print out achievements. Moreover, children can track their progress in real-time and see how far they have come on their learning journey.

If you would like to come up with your play-based speech therapy games at home, consider the following activities commonly used by therapists:

1. **Pretend play**

Pretend play, also known as role-playing, is an effective activity to promote language development. The aim is to get your child talking by creating fictional scenarios and acting them out together. The scenarios you choose can be related to the type of vocabulary you would like your child to learn. For example, if you want your child to learn about different foods, your fictional scenario can take place at a grocery store.

2. **Storytelling**

Storytelling is another language development activity that is great for teaching your child how to communicate effectively. By telling stories (real or made up), they can learn how to use a combination of short and long sentences, order events in the correct sequence, describe characters using various adjectives, and explain the action taking place fluently and concisely.

3. **Sing along to nursery rhymes**

Nursery rhymes can be a fun way to practice speech development and learn how to pronounce syllables and words correctly. What makes nursery rhymes effective is that they have a repetitive structure and encourage your child to remember words. They also encourage your child to repeat

53

different speech sounds like "moo" and "ee-ie ee-ie oh" which improve their mouth and tongue movements.

4. Obstacle courses

At-home obstacle courses are an active and fun way to teach your child how to follow commands and instructions. The nature of the obstacle course should allow them to practice taking different directions like crawling under the table or taking a right turn when instructed. Before taking them through the obstacle course, teach your child a few simple prompts they will need to follow. Use these prompts repetitively during the obstacle course.

The most important thing to remember when planning play-based speech therapy activities for your child is to have fun. If you are enjoying the experience of creating these interactive activities, your child will likely enjoy them too. Take this as an opportunity to tap into your imagination and think like a child. What type of activities would they find entertaining and rewarding?

How to Create a Play-Based Learning Environment at Home

Speech and language development should not be restricted to the classroom or therapy room. Since your child spends most of their time at home, it is important to modify your living space to promote play-based learning.

In the next chapter, we will take a closer look at improving the home environment to enhance your child's growth and learning, but for now, we will look at strategies specifically to encourage play-based speech and language development at home.

Take a moment to think about what a play-based learning environment should ideally look and feel like. What elements should be included to motivate your child to engage in various activities? Write down a few of your ideas in a notebook.

Some of your ideas may include adding visual elements, incorporating technology, creating a designated play-and-learn area, and of course, having diverse toys and games. These are all wonderful ideas that can enhance your play-based learning environment. They can make your child feel calm, supported, and inspired to learn at their own pace and time.

To create more structure for your child, you can incorporate these elements of play into a personalized play-based program. The program will ensure that you balance entertainment with education and reinforce as many speech and language skills as possible while your child is having fun.

Designing this program can also make you feel comfortable taking a step back and allowing your child the freedom to choose how they want to play. Since your home environment is already tailored for learning, you don't need to interrupt or direct their every move as often.

Don't be overwhelmed by the planning involved in creating a personalized play-based learning program. You don't need to be a qualified therapist to curate your home environment to accommodate your child's needs. What matters most is being intentional about creating a space that a young child would find stimulating and supportive, so they can activate their desire to learn!

There are three steps or considerations to make when building your at-home play-based learning program:

Reflect on the Environment

Your home environment can encourage or discourage learning. This is because your child is influenced by the information received through their five senses. Think about the quality of information your child processes through their sense of sight, hearing, smell, touch, and taste. Is this information conducive or disruptive to learning?

A basic example is the visual appeal of your household. If your child is a visual learner, they require bright and colorful posters, diagrams, picture books, and displays to process and memorize information. Updating your home to include visual tools and supplies in areas your child frequently visits can activate their brain. Imagine the impact of having letters of the alphabet on posters or as physical toys or common prompts like "No running" and "Say please and thank you" written in big and bold print in the passageway.

If your child is an auditory learner, meaning they process and memorize information better through listening to sounds and conversations, consider updating the auditory experience at home. For example, enforce family rules about noise levels to keep the atmosphere calm and controlled. You can also incorporate jingles, music, audiobooks, and recordings into your child's daily learning.

For example, read stories aloud, play sing-along nursery rhymes, or have them repeat speech sounds from a tape recording. Your child will find it easier to learn and remember words by hearing them played over and over again than by reading them silently in their head or seeing them displayed on a poster.

Here are a few more tips when it comes to turning your home into a play-based learning environment:

- Clear the clutter and organize learning materials in appropriate storage boxes.

- Draw back the curtains and let the natural sunlight in.

- Switch off the TV during the day (or during learning hours).

- Consider adding room diffusers to clear the air and create a calming effect.

- Laminate wall posters to prevent wear and tear.

- Make sure learning materials are easily accessible to your child (within reach) and thoughtfully arranged to encourage engagement.

- Showcase your child's work and accomplishments throughout the house to celebrate progress and boost their self-esteem.

- Don't forget to take learning outdoors by creating opportunities to explore the garden, move the body, and expand nature vocabulary.

Understand the Needs of Your Child

An effective play-based learning program considers your child's speech and language problem areas and tailor learning material and activities to address those challenges. For example, if your child has difficulty articulating sounds and words properly, they may benefit from seeing and hearing different speech sounds regularly throughout the day.

Besides developmental needs, your child may have a particular learning style they respond favorably to or special interests they naturally gravitate toward. Knowing this information and curating your home environment accordingly can offer your child the support and motivation they need to improve their speech and language.

What's important to remember about understanding your child's needs is that you are more likely to get positive feedback when your home environment appeals to their desires. Take the time to understand your child's strengths and weaknesses or learn about unique personality quirks that inform what they find interesting.

Below are a few tips on how to create a play-based home environment that caters to your child's needs:

- **Provide choice and autonomy:** Play-based learning is mostly self-directed, which means that your child gets the freedom to choose which activities they want to engage with.

- **Leave room for interpretation:** It is expected for some activities to come with rules; however, don't be too fixed on your child adhering to them. Allow room for self-expression so that your child can fully engage with activities and feel successful doing so!

- **Get involved in the fun:** The best way for your child to practice communication skills is during play activities. However, they need a partner to bounce ideas onto and engage in conversation. Ensure that you include some activities that require one-on-one and group social interaction and encourage the whole family to get involved.

- **Play the role of supervisor:** To maximize engagement in learning activities, your child should lead while you observe them play. Younger children may need more guidance at the beginning of tasks and encouragement during tasks to stay focused. Older children may benefit from hearing feedback from you, such as suggestions on how they can improve or praise for their good efforts.

Note that as your child improves their speech and language skills, their needs and preferences can change. Keep your home environment flexible and adaptable to your child's development to ensure they continue to engage in learning.

Establish Clear Goals and Objectives

Play-based learning programs are structured around clear goals and objectives. This is crucial for making sure you select games and activities with intention. Additionally, clear goals enforce a sense of accountability in your child and serve as a constant reminder of what is expected of them.

For a young person who may not understand how to read written goals, consider making visual illustrations with images and diagrams to help them understand learning intentions or desired results.

For example, if your goal is to teach your child how to pronounce the word "Apple" correctly, you might create a poster that spells out the word, offers a visual representation of an apple, and provides a breakdown of syllables to help your child pronounce the word.

Another way to communicate learning goals and objectives with your child is to spend a few minutes explaining the purpose of an activity before your child starts playing. Using simple language, help them understand what is expected of them and what success may look like. Perhaps you can do a quick demonstration of how to play the game then ask your child to do the same while you watch.

Lastly, make sure that you plan appropriate rewards for the successful completion of learning goals. These rewards don't have to be big; however, they must carry significance. For instance, you can create a reward chart that acknowledges the progress your child makes toward speech and language milestones. Every time your child completes an activity, you can reward them with a sticker that is placed on their rewards chart. After collecting a certain number of stickers, they can choose a sweet prize!

These three steps or considerations will help you build a successful play-based learning program at home that supports your child's speech and language development goals. Remember to personalize your program according to your child's interests and needs to enhance their learning experience.

Key Takeaway

Play is an essential part of your child's cognitive and social development. Through play, your child learns how to solve problems, memorize information, communicate effectively, and build self-confidence. Play-based speech therapy uses age-appropriate games and activities to introduce and reinforce speech and language skills. The benefit of this approach is that your child is encouraged to practice communication skills without feeling pressured to. To practice play-based learning at home, take the time to create a personalized program for your child that considers environmental factors and specific needs and goals.

Chapter 5:

Creating the Ideal Home

Environment to Support Your

Child's Development

Nurturing an inclusive culture begins in the family. Home is the first place
to foster openness and a culture of inclusion.
—Alain Dehaze

The Importance of Parenting Approaches in Early Childhood Development

In the previous chapter, we discussed the importance of play in speech therapy and how play-based learning at home can enhance your child's speech and language development. In this chapter, we are staying on the subject of improving the home environment; however, we will focus on parenting strategies to create a healthy and learning-conducive environment.

This chapter will be particularly eye-opening if it is your first time raising a child with developmental delays or learning disabilities. You may have questions about disciplining your child, helping them cultivate healthy self-esteem, or finding ways to make them feel included in the family.

The strategies you are about to learn will not only show you how to create a safe and nurturing environment at home but also how to raise a confident and independent child who isn't negatively affected by their developmental challenges.

A responsive, supportive, and nurturing home environment is a key component of early childhood learning and development. The events and experiences that children are exposed to as infants, toddlers, and preschoolers leave a lifelong imprint on their minds.

Studies show that adverse childhood experiences, such as exposure to stressful or traumatic situations, can cause disruptions to a child's neurological development (Savage, 2014). These brain changes can be temporary or permanent depending on the nature of the adverse experience and the length of exposure.

When important areas of the brain are damaged or not functioning optimally, the affected child may have difficulty regulating emotions, coping with stress, concentrating on tasks, communicating effectively, and learning.

Sometimes parents unintentionally expose their children to stress or trauma by not being aware of the impact of their behaviors or the quality of the environment at home. For example, yelling or using other aggressive tactics to discipline children can be perceived by them as criticism or rejection.

The same goes for making decisions on behalf of children. While this may seem like a good thing, especially when parenting late-talkers, it can be perceived by children as controlling and a deliberate attempt to take away their freedom and autonomy. Over time, children who are not permitted to make decisions on their own may let out their frustration by misbehaving and being uncooperative when reprimanded by their parents.

What you believe is right and justified for raising your child may be perceived to them as punitive, unloving, and unsupportive. It is, therefore, important to regularly assess the extent to which your parenting approach enables your child to become the best version of themselves.

The Ideal Parenting Style for Children With Speech Delays and Disabilities

There is no such thing as a "perfect parent," since perfection doesn't exist. Parents are human beings who make mistakes and learn through experience. Nevertheless, there is such a thing as advantageous and disadvantageous parenting.

Advantageous parenting is conscious and responsible parenting that encourages thoughtful and empathetic decision-making to provide a safe and nurturing environment for the child. Disadvantageous parenting is reactive parenting that makes decisions based on how the parent feels rather than what is in the best interest of the child.

While we don't support seeking perfection, we do recommend adjusting your parenting approach to encourage advantageous parenting. Children with speech delays and other disabilities require a lot of support, affection, and patience. This may sound like a tall order, but with the correct parenting approach, it can be achieved effortlessly.

Experts agree that children with disabilities who are raised with the positive parenting approach display higher levels of independence, social interaction, emotional expression, and language skills compared to those who are raised with alternative parenting approaches (Morgenegg, 2013).

Positive parenting, or authoritative parenting, is a parenting style that balances setting and enforcing boundaries with providing children the space and freedom to become their own person. Parents use mistakes and troublesome behavior as teachable moments to guide children on how to make better decisions.

Parents who use this approach show respect for their children's self-will but balance this with setting parameters and expectations for what the child should and should not aim for. As a result, children raised in this type of environment exhibit a strong sense of self, healthy boundaries, and effective communication and assertiveness skills.

There are three positive parenting rules to remember that can promote a stronger relationship with your child. The first rule is to make your expectations clear, and for a child with speech delays (who may or may not have trouble listening), this means offering instructions in multiple ways.

For example, you might look your child in the eyes and slowly tell them what you need. Thereafter, you might use nonverbal communication through gestures to convey the same message. Alternatively, you can draw a diagram to illustrate the message to a visual learner. These are all prompts to help your child follow instructions and offer as much support as possible.

The second positive parenting rule is to be consistent and reliable. Simply put, don't make promises that you cannot keep or don't introduce your child to activities that you cannot maintain in the long term. Since your child is catching up on learning, they need a predictable environment to enhance their memory and encourage pattern recognition. Keep exercises and routines simple and easy to follow so that your child finds the process of learning manageable.

The third positive parenting rule is to seek to understand where your child is coming from. Come from a place of empathy and compassion, even when they are misbehaving. Ask yourself, "What might my child be feeling right now?" Remember that speech delays can be frustrating for children who are eager to speak or have started school and feel challenged by the increasing expectations. Older children may experience social pressure and bullying for not being able to communicate as fluently as other children.

The following section will delve deeper into positive parenting by presenting five strategies to improve your home environment and get positive feedback from your child.

Six Positive Parenting Strategies to Make Your Child Feel Comfortable at Home

Positive parenting teaches you to focus on the solution rather than the problem presented in front of you. When your child throws a tantrum, for example, the problem is their inappropriate emotional outburst, but the solution is identifying your child's unmet needs at that moment.

Let's say your child refuses to sit down and practice speech exercises when they return home from school. The problem is their public act of defiance, but the solution is adapting to their present need for play and finding exhilarating ways to practice speech exercises that don't feel like work.

The following six positive parenting strategies are examples of solutions that support your child's social, cognitive, and emotional development. They are also effective in relieving stress and anxiety and reducing the frequency of meltdowns and other explosive behaviors.

As you go through these six strategies, remind yourself of the three golden rules of positive parenting, which are making your expectations clear, being consistent and reliable, and seeking to understand where your child is coming from. Practicing these rules alongside the strategies provided will enhance the quality of your interactions with your child.

Practice Responsive Caregiving

Responsive caregiving refers to tuning into the unexpressed needs, emotions, and desires of your child and responding with appropriate behaviors. Older children may verbalize what they need or how they feel in direct or indirect ways. These are known as bids. Your task as their parent is to recognize when your child is making a bid and respond by giving them what they need.

For example, restless behavior like whining, complaining, or crying unnecessarily can be a bid for affection or attention. Your child may simply want you to pick them up or go down to their level and ask if they are tired, hungry, bored, or need a cuddle.

Responsive caregiving is particularly important when parenting a child with speech delays because they may not have an expansive vocabulary or sufficient grammar skills to ask for what they need. You will need to study your child and understand their personality and preferences to be able to anticipate and respond promptly to their needs.

There are several ways of developing a close relationship with your child to become more in tune with what they need. One option is to mirror their behaviors and reciprocate the feedback they give. For example, when they point at a character in a book and display amazement, mirror the same facial expression and point at the character too. Or when they smile at you, smile back with the same enthusiasm.

Another option is to spend more time playing and completing tasks with your child. For instance, assist your older child in sorting through their closet and putting aside old clothes. Or when creating a shopping list, ask them to help you brainstorm food items to purchase.

Attending to the same tasks as your child allows you to see how well they perform in different contexts. Over time, you can pick up on behaviors they find pleasant or unpleasant, topics they prefer or avoid, and experiences that motivate them to talk openly.

Foster Feelings of Competence

Speech delays can affect your child's self-esteem, particularly when they start elementary school and struggle with basic literacy skills. To ensure your child maintains an open and curious mind, they must feel a sense of competence in their ability to communicate.

Competence refers to the ability to do something well. When your child feels competent, they believe that they are capable of accomplishing a task or goal. What's important is believing that they can because that is the motivation your child needs to get up and try. The irony about competence is that without self-belief, your child will never know what they are capable of achieving.

Therefore, your child must visualize success to be inspired to work toward it. They must be able to envision themselves speaking fluently and being received positively by others to be encouraged to show up that way.

One way to help your child feel like a good communicator is to speak to them like one. When interacting with them, forget that they do not have a wide vocabulary or proficient grammar skills and speak to them as they understand. Ask open-ended questions that solicit feedback and validate their responses. Show respect toward what they say and acknowledge their opinions. Soon enough, your child will feel empowered to share their thoughts and feelings because they feel like good communicators.

Another great strategy is to allow your child to speak without interrupting them. Listen carefully and nod or smile to show that you are engaged with what they are saying. When your child experiences difficulty during speech exercises, resist the urge to step in. Sit silently and wait for them to gather their thoughts and complete the prompt. Doing this teaches your child to solve their problems, and the more problems they solve, the more competent they feel.

Lastly, positive affirmations are crucial when building your child's sense of competence. There will be times when your child doesn't feel like a winner and may need to be reminded they are one. Make it a habit to look for opportunities to praise your child and celebrate their milestones. Introduce a rewards chart that allows them to visually see the progress they are making. Another fun idea is to celebrate major milestones by printing out certificates and hanging them up in your child's room.

Feeling competent doesn't happen overnight. It takes plenty of positive evidence for your child to believe in themselves. Challenge yourself to get better at identifying positive behaviors that prove your child is becoming a better communicator and celebrate these moments with them.

Increase Engagement During Home Learning

A great way to motivate your child to continue practicing speech and language skills at home is to create an environment that promotes learning. In the previous chapter, we spoke about the benefit of a play-based learning program at home. While this sounds great on paper, your child needs to desire to learn in order to implement this strategy.

Your parenting approach plays a significant role in shaping your child's attitudes toward learning. The more space and freedom you allow for their natural curiosity to come forth, the more open they will be to discover new ideas and concepts. There are other useful tips to remember whenever you seek to increase your child's engagement in at-home learning:

1. Don't make it feel like a classroom

Learning at home should not look or feel similar to formal education at school. You don't need to plan every speech or language lesson to detail or worry about achieving learning outcomes. Home is where your child gets to relax and be themselves. Thus, to make learning at home fun, it must be based on your child's interests, desires, and preferred forms of entertainment. Having fun may not always be the goal in the classroom, but at home, everything you do revolves around it!

2. Make learning a social activity

Individual speech and language practice is important; however, the best way for your child to test their skills is to communicate with diverse people. Create plenty of opportunities to practice speech and language activities as a family or with different groups of friends. For example, whenever you invite kids over for a play date, have a few fun and interactive group activities planned that promote speaking skills.

3. Follow their lead

Learning is fun when your child is motivated to do it. When they are not in the mood to complete speech exercises, allow them to take a break or play outside until they are ready to put their thinking cap back on. It is also important to take directions from your child about how to structure their learning time. For example, if they complain about sitting down for too long, find ways to incorporate physical activity into the lesson. For a variety of fun and interactive games and activities, head over to the last three chapters of the book!

4. Link learning to the outside world

Older children are more likely to stay engaged in learning at home when the lessons or activities offered are related to real-world experiences. For example, if you want to practice conversation skills with your middle school child, you can role-play a realistic interaction they would have with their friends at school. Or whenever you are teaching your child new vocabulary, focus on themes they are likely to be exposed to in the outside world. For example, you might teach your child vocabulary around finances, shopping, self-defense, or setting boundaries.

For children with speech delays and challenges, the home counts as another learning environment where their skills are developed. However, if learning at home is not engaging, they are less likely to be motivated to participate. Make learning at home work for them and feel relevant to their learning style and preferences.

Promote Inclusion at Home

Inclusion refers to making sure everyone feels accepted and valued for who they are and what they can contribute within a group setting. Inclusion at home is about recognizing the inherent worth of every member of your family, from the youngest to the oldest.

Being a late talker comes with its challenges and often makes the affected child feel like an outsider. This is more common when the child has siblings who can communicate without difficulty. As a parent, your job is to not necessarily treat all of your children the same, but instead make every child feel accepted for who they are.

Fostering a sense of belonging can make family members feel like they have a place in the home. A great way to foster a sense of belonging is to unite the family over shared beliefs and values; principles that can be understood and upheld by everyone. For example, you may want to create family rules, and unique traditions, or identify special occasions and celebrations in the year that matter to the family.

Promoting inclusion at home is also about creating a safe environment to have tough conversations like acknowledging differences. Children are smart enough to make comparisons and notice when a sibling is not exhibiting the same behaviors.

Instead of pretending that these differences don't exist, bring them up in an open discussion and allow your children to ask questions. If you don't have expert knowledge to answer some questions, consult with your pediatrician or SLP and ask for guidance on how to approach certain topics.

Take a few minutes to reflect on how inclusive your household is of every family member. Think of the unique needs of your spouse, children, and pets, and answer the following questions:

- How well does your household celebrate differences?

- Are house rules considerate of every member's needs and interests?

- Are family activities diverse and reflective of your family values?

- Is every member of your family encouraged to participate in group activities or share their thoughts during group discussions?

Decrease Challenging Behavior With Redirecting Behaviors

It is normal for a child with speech delays or impediments to develop behavioral issues due to the growing frustration of not being able to communicate effectively. But reprimanding them every time they seek to express their frustration will only make them feel invalidated.

This doesn't mean that you shouldn't discipline a child who behaves inappropriately. However, how you choose to discipline them matters. In general, positive parenting speaks against traditional forms of discipline, which may include yelling, spanking, or grounding (i.e., putting children in timeouts). Instead, it promotes positive discipline which is correcting a child's behavior in a manner that inspires learning and motivates the child to make better choices.

There are several ways to enforce positive discipline but one specific strategy that we will look at is redirecting behavior. The goal of redirecting behavior is to shift your child's focus away from undesirable actions and toward neutral or positive actions.

Making this shift interrupts negative patterns of behavior and promotes better decision-making. In a sense, you can show your child what desirable behavior looks like, and hopefully, over time they can choose this behavior for themselves.

Additionally, redirecting behavior teaches your child how to self-regulate and look for better coping skills to manage stress than acting out. For example, if your child is fighting over a toy with their sibling, removing the toy from the environment can deescalate the situation and give both children an opportunity to calm down.

It is worth noting that redirecting behaviors look different based on your child's age and the situation at hand. Below are a few examples of different techniques you can practice.

1. Present choices

When your child is emotional, they are unable to think logically about the next steps. To help them make better decisions, offer them two positive choices to improve the situation. For example, if your child is upset about being told they can't play outside you can present two choices for indoor activities they will likely enjoy.

2. Ignore attention-seeking behaviors

When you notice that your child is misbehaving as a form of rebellion, pretend you are not disturbed by the behavior. Continue with the task you were busy with and distract yourself until the attention-seeking behavior stops. Once they have calmed down, walk over to your child and give them positive attention to reward their self-control.

3. Redirect energy

It is normal for children to have a lot of pent-up energy that comes out as explosive behaviors, more so when they are not getting enough physical activity during the day. Whenever you sense that your child's misbehavior is due to containing fiery energy, redirect their energy to positive adrenaline-filled activities like participating in obstacle courses outside, playing a kid-friendly dance workout, or getting them to sing along to karaoke tunes.

Since your child is still learning to regulate their emotions and control impulses, they need support to practice desirable behaviors. Redirecting behaviors can teach your child positive coping skills that can turn into new habits.

Provide Structure and Routine

Structure and routine are essential for a child with developmental delays. This is because they require more practice and repetition to learn what comes almost naturally to other children. Having predictable timetables at home can be a positive way to encourage your child to develop critical social, cognitive, and speaking skills.

Remember, also, that to create a play-based learning environment at home, it is important to keep your child's brain active. Creating structure and routine helps to plan your child's day around educational activities, some incorporating speech and language skills, so they can remain productive.

Another consideration to make is that your late-talking child may be prone to feeling anxious or stressed whenever they are presented with unexpected tasks that put them outside of their comfort zone. Due to their communication challenges, they may feel at a disadvantage whenever they can't anticipate what is going to happen or what may be expected of them.

Getting your child accustomed to predictable activities during the week can put their mind at ease and allow them to be more open to taking in new information. However, when introducing your child to routines, take the time to explain their daily schedule.

Use different formats, such as calendars, posters, and charts to visually communicate what is expected of them. You may even role-play daily activities with your child like brushing your teeth or sleeping to make learning the new routine fun.

Lastly, take advantage of daily routines, like lunchtime or bathtime, to practice relatable speech and language exercises. For instance, lunchtime can be dedicated to expanding your child's vocabulary about mealtimes, healthy eating, and the digestive system. You may also reinforce good table manners and appropriate social behaviors.

Key Takeaway

Your relationship with your child plays a critical role in their development. It is worth reflecting on how your parenting approach supports your child in their growth and learning. Consider the benefits of adopting the principles of positive parenting, which focus attention on desirable behaviors (rather than undesirable behaviors) and seek to find solutions to troublesome behaviors. Moreover, reflect on how you promote responsive caregiving, a sense of competence, inclusivity, and predictable routines at home.

Chapter 6:

Speech Games and Activities

for Children Aged 3-5

We worry about what a child will become tomorrow, yet we forget that he is someone today.
—Stacia Tauscher

What Speech Therapy for Children Aged 3-5 Looks Like

Experts agree the earlier you start to introduce your child to speech and language skills, the easier it is for him or her to grasp and remember them. Moreover, starting with training at a young age can improve your child's speaking abilities significantly by the time they start elementary school.

You don't need to wait until you get a diagnosis to address minor speech errors. Maybe your child is showing normal signs of delayed speech like recalling a few words or not pronouncing their words properly. They are still a good candidate for speech therapy exercises!

The following fun and interactive games and activities are designed for children aged 3-5 who need additional practice to reach age-appropriate speech and language milestones. You will notice that some activities are structured while others are unstructured. Both types of activities support play-based learning and offer your child plenty of room to explore and enjoy the process of becoming a better communicator.

20 Fun and Interactive Speech-Language Games and Activities

Complete the following activities in the order you prefer. Since you know your child best, you are welcome to personalize any of these activities to match their interests and preferences. Remember that while instructions are important to follow, your child has the freedom to interpret these activities however they like.

Lastly, have fun teaching and guiding your child along this journey!

Activity 1: Flashcard Fun

Flashcards are educational tools to help small children recognize and memorize speech and language. What makes them effective for teaching is that they include a visual and written element.

For example, a flashcard may have the sound "Ah" written at the top, followed by a picture of a juicy apple, and then a breakdown of the word "Ah-Puhl." Your child learns a few things by looking at this flashcard, such as how to pronounce the sound "Ah" and the appropriate way to use it in a word. They also learn to make an association between the fruit and the sound.

Switch up your flashcards by adding a physical element. For example, after prompting your child to pronounce the sound "Ah" and the word "Apple," ask them to show you how an apple is eaten.

You can purchase a pack of language-learning flashcards online on sites like *SpeechBuddy.com* or create your flashcards using art supplies or graphic design tools like Canva. Create themed sets of cards to introduce your child to a wide range of vocabulary.

Activity 2: Story Cubes

Story cubes are picture-based blocks that are used for learning and reviewing language. For children who can use three or more words in a sentence, story cubes can introduce them to simple sentence structures and storytelling skills.

For example, you might instruct your child to roll a story cube and use the image shown to complete the following sentence: "I like to..." The completed sentence might say, "I like to paint" (if the image is a picture of a paintbrush).

Another way to use story cubes is to act out an action related to the image shown on the block. For example, if the image is of an airplane, you can ask your child to act as though they were an airplane flying in the sky.

You can purchase story cubes from Amazon or make your cubes by copying a free 3D template on cardboard paper, cutting out the cube, and gluing together the folds. On each side of the cube, paste easy-to-interpret colorful pictures of common household, nature, school, or shopping items.

Activity 3: Pretend Play With Dolls or Action Figures

Pretend play encourages your child to act out various situations. In doing so, they can practice using new words, pronouncing sounds, and words accurately, and speaking like people they admire. Not only can this be a great confidence booster, but it helps your child learn appropriate social cues and communication behaviors.

For example, if your child is pretending to be a doctor, they are encouraged to practice greetings, asking questions, making commands (e.g., "breathe in and out"), problem-solving (e.g., diagnosing their patient), and showing empathy toward others.

Pretend play is mostly unstructured and leaves a lot of the details to your child's interpretation. Nevertheless, to make the game fun, invest in props, dress-up outfits, and all sorts of accessories to help your child think out of the box and learn new words. Find items around your home that you no longer use like old wooden spoons, jewelry, neckties, and wallets. Place them all in a large storage box for the next time your child decides to engage in pretend play.

Activity 4: Articulation Practice with Silly Sentences

Between the ages of 3-5, your child still enjoys goofing around. They can't help themselves! What better way to help your child practice different mouth and tongue movements than by acting silly with them?

Articulation practices involve making different sounds or combinations of sounds using your lips, teeth, tongue, and palate. The aim is not to create real words but instead to practice pronouncing syllables and vowels that are used to construct words.

If your child is already in speech therapy, ask their SLP to provide you with targeted sounds to practice at home each week. Alternatively, you can download a speech sounds developmental chart that shows what sounds your child should be able to pronounce in words at each age. Below is an example:

Age	Speech sound milestone
3 years	/p/, /b/, /m/, /n/, /t/, /d/
4 years	/p/, /b/, /m/, /n/, /t/, /d/, /k/, /g/, /f/, /s/, /y/, /h/
5 years	/p/, /b/, /m/, /n/, /t/, /d/, /k/, /g/, /f/, /s/, /y/, /h/, /sh/, /ch/, /j, /z/, /l/, /v/

Remember to provide positive reinforcement after every successful attempt. When your child doesn't pronounce the sound correctly, calmly repeat the sound slowly until they say it correctly. Don't be afraid to make different facial expressions and mouth movements to improve your articulation of the sound.

Activity 5: Simon Says

Simon Says is a fun instructional game that tests your child's listening skills and ability to follow instructions. It can also reveal how much vocabulary your child can grasp. The simple rule is for your child to do whatever Simon (who will be played by you) commands. Each command begins with the phrase "Simon says..." followed by the instruction you would like them to follow.

Simple phrases to use with your child may focus on making simple body movements. For example:

- Simon says, "Clap your hands."

- Simon says, "Sit down."

- Simon says to stomp your feet.

If your child struggles to recognize the action that needs to be taken, model it in front of them. Once they learn how to follow a single direction, you can ask them to follow two directions. Here are some examples:

- Simon says, "Smile and wave."

- Simon says, "Sit down and cross your legs."

- Simon says, "Clap your hands and stomp your feet."

This game works when practicing speech too. For example, you might ask your child to play the role of Simon if you want them to practice saying the "S" sound. Alternatively, you can have a variety of flashcards with speech cards on the floor and instruct them to identify and pick up a specific sound. For example, you might say, "Simon says find and pick up the "R" sound."

Activity 6: Reading Picture Books

Reading picture books to your child is a great way to practice different kinds of speech and language skills. For example, by reading to them, your child can learn new words and the pronunciation of various sounds. You may decide to get them to read after you so they can practice expressive language. Books expose your child to interesting storylines that can be used at the end to practice comprehension skills. For instance, you might ask your child questions about the characters, the setting of the story, or the perceptions and feelings of the characters.

There are other interactive ways to use picture books to practice speech and language recognition, such as:

- asking your child to follow directions (e.g., "Point to the sun.")

- understanding prepositions (e.g., "What object is on top of the table?")

- practicing numeracy (e.g., "How many people can you see on the page?")

- making predictions and creating narratives (e.g., "What do you think is going to happen on the next page?")

- practicing target speech sounds (e.g., "This is a school. What sound does "school" start with?")

Activity 7: Rhyming Word Puzzles

Phonological awareness is the ability to recognize and identify parts of words and sentences. It can be taught in several ways, such as getting your child to count, categorize words that contain similar sounds, and find rhyming words.

Rhyming word puzzles help your child sort through and match words that rhyme. They encourage your child to use their problem-solving skills to determine which words fall under the same word family. For example, words that fall under the "at" word family include cat, bat, mat, rat, and sat. Their challenge would be to recognize words from the same word family and match them.

You can purchase rhyming puzzles on Amazon or get creative and create your puzzles by printing square blocks with two rhyming words (and images for visual aid) diagonally to each other. Leave enough space between the words to cut through the middle with scissors to make two puzzle pieces. Scatter the puzzle pieces in front of your child and ask them to identify the matching words.

Activity 8: Turn-Taking Storytelling

Taking turns is an important social skill that children aged 3-5 ought to learn to develop friendships. One way to teach your child how to take turns while practicing grammar and language skills is to play a game of turn-taking storytelling. The game aims to go back-and-forth with your child building a single story by taking turns creating sentences.

Start by explaining the process to your child. You can role-play with an older sibling or adult in the house to show your child what is expected of them. Once the process has been explained, begin the game with a simple sentence like, "Once upon a time, there was a little girl who had a dog named Spotty." Indicate to your child that it is their turn and ask them to continue telling the story using their own words.

If possible, follow a similar storyline structure as the books your child frequently reads to make it easier for them to recognize how to develop the story. Taking turns is a crucial element of the game. You can decide whether to use language like, "It's my turn," or pass a talking stick (i.e., hairbrush or wooden spoon) to indicate whose turn it is. If your child has not learned the words "my" and "your," use actual names. For instance, you can say, "It's Mommy's turn," and "It's Josh's turn."

Activity 9: Scavenger Hunt for Objects

A scavenger hunt allows your child to get some indoor physical activity while practicing speech and language skills. The aim is to help your child review new vocabulary they have learned by getting them to search for physical objects around the house.

To simplify the game, focus on words that fit under a theme. For example, if your child has recently learned about animals, center the scavenger hunt around finding animal objects around the house. Another way to simplify the game is to restrict the scavenger hunt to a room or area of the house, such as their bedroom or kitchen pantry.

Before you start the scavenger hunt, give your child a list or flashcards with objects they need to look for. Encourage them to refer to their list or flashcards for guidance. If you decide to offer a list of objects, make sure there is a photo of the object for visual assistance.

Allow your child to lead the scavenger hunt; however, be there to supervise the activity, especially when the hunt is taking place outdoors or in areas of the house that may be unsafe for children to explore alone like the garage or kitchen.

Activity 10: Song Lyrics and Rhymes

Nursery rhymes are a great way to teach your child phonological awareness and make them feel competent in their ability to use language. The best part is that nursery rhymes are entertaining and give your child enough room to express themselves. When repeated continuously, nursery rhymes can help your child form sentences, practice grammar skills, and improve control over their voice.

There are a few tips to remember when teaching nursery rhymes to your child:

- **Don't worry if you are singing alone.** It may take your child a while before they can repeat nursery rhymes. Continue to sing them with the same melody to strengthen their memory.

- **Use your whole face and body.** Being animated when teaching nursery rhymes can help your child recall the song better. Plus, they can associate different facial expressions or gestures with particular sounds or words in the song.

- **Consistency is key.** How you choose to introduce a nursery rhyme should become how you sing the song going forward. Remaining consistent helps your child separate different nursery rhymes and memorize a larger pool of words and phrases.

Activity 11: Conversation Cards

A conversation is a dialogue between two or more people where ideas are exchanged. Between the ages of 3-5, your child is beginning to learn how to form sentences with three or more words and engage in conversations.

Conversation cards are a great way to help your child form longer sentences and keep a conversation going for at least two back-and-forth exchanges. Other skills taught and reinforced through conversation cards are emotional regulation, social behaviors like smiling and asking follow-up questions, and non-verbal communication like maintaining eye contact.

You can purchase conversation cards online or create your own. If you decide to create them, keep the cards simple by including a short conversation starter like, "Tell me about your family," or "What are your favorite foods?" If your child is still too young to understand prompts, create conversation cards with simple images. When your child picks up a card, they must spend at least 10 seconds speaking about the image. For example, they can describe the image, tell a story about it, or state their opinion about it (e.g., whether or not they like the object represented in the image, and why).

Activity 12: Category Sorting

Teaching your child category sorting makes it easier to process and memorize information without feeling overwhelmed. For instance, instead of seeing words as being standalone, your child can recognize them by their function, meaning, or similar associations.

Moreover, it makes it easier for your child to identify differences between words and sounds. For example, an orange and a carrot fit under the same color category; however, one is a fruit and the other is a vegetable. Therefore, when teaching your child vocabulary about colors, you may group oranges and carrots, but place them in different categories when teaching your child vocabulary about fruits and vegetables.

The best way to create categories is by utilizing flashcards or separate storage bins. For example, you might play a game of category sorting by placing an empty bin in front of your child and asking them to fill it up with green objects in the playroom. Or you might scatter flashcards in front of them and ask them to put aside flashcards that show food items.

You can also switch things up by placing three flashcards in front of your child and asking them to identify the odd one out (a card that doesn't match the others). For example, if you have a card with a bus, garden rake, and car, the garden rake would be the odd one out because it is not a form of transportation.

Activity 13: Sequencing Activities

Life unfolds in sequences. There is a past, present, and future; morning, afternoon, and evening. Your child must start practicing how to recognize sequences at this age because this will help them develop better communication skills later down the line. For now, what is important to know is that everything has a beginning, middle, and end, or occurs in order (i.e., step 1, step 2, and step 3).

A simple sequencing activity to practice is presenting your child with a picture of an action taking place, such as a young child brushing their teeth. Thereafter, ask them, "What comes next?" This prompt should help them guess the following action. If they struggle to provide the next steps, ask them to think about what they usually do after performing a similar action. You might say, "What do you do after brushing your teeth?"

This exercise continues until your child cannot think of a logical next step or when they arrive back at the first step. Here is an example of the process:

Parent: Here is a picture of a boy brushing his teeth. What comes next?

Child: He eats cereal.

Parent: Then what does he do?

Child: He puts his bowl away.

Parent: What happens after that?

Activity 14: Build a Mini Dictionary

Keep track of your child's growing vocabulary by creating a mini dictionary with words they fully understand and can use in a sentence. Use the dictionary as part of your daily speech and language practice by creating activities that promote the use of those learned words.

Remember, by age three, your child is expected to be able to pronounce 500 words and recognize more than 1,000 words. By age five, your child is expected to recognize 10,000 words (Law et al., 2016). Thus, creating a mini dictionary not only helps you keep track of how many words your child can say or recognize but also motivates you to set vocabulary goals and milestones.

For example, you might set a goal to learn 25 new words each week (i.e., 100 words per month). Have a spot quiz at the end of each week and once a month to test your child's understanding of new words and make sure they can pronounce them correctly or use them in a simple sentence. Reward them for reaching the 100-word milestone every month by allowing them to choose their prize out of a bag of goodies.

Activity 15: Speech Sound Bingo

If you are searching for an out-of-the-box articulation and language game to play with your child, speech sound bingo is the one for you! The same rules of bingo apply; however, this one comes with a twist. Instead of calling out numbers, you call out speech sounds from a deck of cards or slideshow on your tablet. This will prompt your child to look at their bingo card and see whether they have the same sound. If they do, they cross it out; if not, the game continues. The game is won when your child crosses out four or five blocks in a row, either vertically, diagonally, or horizontally (depending on your number of blocks).

To enhance the entertainment aspect of the game, invite a few more young people similar to your child's age to participate and turn it into a group activity. Preferably, choose children who are at the same speech development level so that the game is equally challenging for everyone. Remember to reward all participants with a prize when the game ends!

Activity 16: Hide-and-Seek With Sounds

Hide-and-seek is one of those classic games that small children love to play. Fortunately, the rules of the game can be modified to include speech practice. For instance, you can hide a few objects in a room that start with the target speech sounds for the week. If you are teaching your child the "F" sound, you might hide a fan, toy frog, and fruit. Let them know what objects to look for and then start the timer.

When your child gets the hang of this game, switch roles and let them be the one who hides objects. Once again, the objects they hide must start with the target speech sound for a week. Give them enough time to think about the sound, find matching objects, and hide them in secret locations in a room. For instance, you might step away for 10 minutes while they plan what to hide and where to hide it. After the time is up, go back into the room and start the search. The aim is to assess how well your child was able to identify objects that start with the target speech sound.

Activity 17: Barrier Games

Barrier games reinforce listening and comprehension skills. The aim is to create a barrier between you and your child and give them instructions to draw a picture or build an object with Legos. The only tool they have at their disposal is their ears. Repeat the instructions slowly, getting a signal from your child when you can move on to the next step. Go through each step until you have reached the end then break down the barrier and see what your child has produced.

The outcome should look similar to what you had in mind. If you like, you can have a picture already drawn or a Lego structure already constructed before the game starts. Bring out the picture or Lego structure at the very end when looking at the similarities with your child's creation.

For better results, keep the instructions simple and use language your child is familiar with. The barrier can be created by a large pillow held up against your face, a scarf covering your eyes, or sitting on two chairs back-to-back.

Activity 18: Puppet Show

Your child's imagination is running wild during the ages of three to five, which causes them to enjoy pretend play. Staging a puppet show for your child and introducing them to a few of your "sock friends" can be a fun way to get them to talk and practice back-and-forth conversations.

The best part about puppet shows is that you can practice a wide range of speech and language skills. For example, on one occasion, your puppets can teach your child how to pronounce certain sounds and words. On another occasion, your child can teach the puppets how to say words the correct way. Puppet shows can also be used for telling stories, singing nursery rhymes, or taking turns making silly voices with your child.

When your child reaches the age of five, they may be interested in having their puppet. Help them make a sock friend and use the puppets as a buffer to have open conversations with each other. Through your puppet's voice, you can ask your child questions about their desires and fears, envision the future together, and teach them age-appropriate life lessons.

Activity 19: Playdough Articulation

If your child enjoys getting their hands dirty or manipulating materials, playdough articulation can be a fun speech game to play. To get started, you will need small plastic alphabet molds, a ball of playdough, and a small plastic rolling pin. Give your child a few minutes to roll out their playdough into an even sheet. Say the speech sound out loud and ask your child to create the same sound using the alphabet molds.

Your job is to assess how well they follow each step (ideally without a lot of help). For example, you will count how long it takes them to identify the correct alphabet (or alphabet) to match the sounds. If the sound combines two letters, you will assess their ability to order the letters correctly (e.g., the "Sh" sound cannot start with "S," followed by "H").

After every round, congratulate your child for their effort and ask them to mash the playdough into one big ball. Start the game all over again using a different speech sound.

Activity 20: Build a Storyboard

Storyboarding is a technique used to describe the development of a story using picture frames. Each frame provides a snapshot of how the plot thickens and the action unfolds. By looking at the frame collectively, you can gain a better understanding of the beginning, middle, and end of the story.

You can use storyboarding to teach your child sequencing and how to structure stories. Lay out a few story cards on the floor that tell a story. It is recommended to purchase a few sets of story cards online for added convenience. Creating your own cards requires a great deal of planning and design skills.

Begin to tell the story illustrated on the cards using short sentences. Your sentences should clearly describe the action depicted on each card to help your child easily identify the correct one. When they have found the right card, set it aside on your storyboard. Continue to identify the correct cards to describe the sequence of events until you have built a complete storyboard.

At the end, you can ask your child to start from the first frame on the storyboard and retell the whole story using their own words.

Chapter 7:

Speech Games and Activities

for Children Aged 6-8

Every day, in 100 small ways, our children ask, 'Do you hear me? Do you see me? Do I matter?' Their behavior often reflects our response.
    —L.R. Knost

What Speech Therapy for Children Aged 6-8 Looks Like

Children with speech delays or impediments who are between the ages of 6-8 require a slightly different approach to speech therapy. Since they are much older now and have a wider vocabulary, the main goal is to teach them how to become better listeners, follow instructions, start conversations, and read with more clarity and conviction. Essentially, you are building on the speech and language skills that you introduced to them at ages 3-5.

There are two considerations to make when presenting speech and language exercises to a child in this age group. The first is to amplify the entertainment factor of the activities to increase and maintain high engagement. For instance, completing spelling tests or repeating a long list of sounds is something your child may find boring—for lack of a better word. Take your lessons outdoors, include physical components, and allow your child to get messy!

The second consideration to make is that your child may feel more self-conscious about their inability to speak as fluently as other children. Be mindful of this insecurity when guiding them through activities. Offer plenty of positive reinforcement and rewards for progress made. Make them feel like champions for doing their best to communicate effectively.

20 Fun and Interactive Speech-Language Games and Activities

Complete the following activities in the order you prefer. Since you know your child best, you are welcome to personalize any of these activities to match their interests and preferences. Remember that while instructions are important to follow, your child has the freedom to interpret these activities however they like.

Lastly, have fun teaching and guiding your child along this journey!

Activity 1: Synonym/Antonym Match

Now that your child has a larger vocabulary, they are old enough to learn the nuances of language. The simple message to teach them at this stage is that similar words can carry slightly different ideas or meanings. Furthermore, some words are associated with positive thoughts and feelings while other words are associated with negative thoughts and feelings.

A fun game you can introduce to your child is synonym/antonym match. The objective of the game is to match words and adjectives that are similar and/or opposite to each other. A week or two before playing the game, go over adjectives and practice using them in sentences. This will help your child learn the meaning and context of different words.

When playing synonym/antonym match, scatter adjective cards on the floor and give your child five minutes to find synonyms (words that have similar meanings, like "pretty" and "beautiful"). Review their sorting skills and reward them for their effort. If there are any errors, help your child identify the mistake and correct it themselves.

Scatter the cards once more and start the timer. This time, challenge your child to find antonyms (words that have opposite meanings, like "kind" and "mean") in five minutes or less. Go through the same review process and reward your child for their efforts.

Activity 2: Guess the Word

A new skill that your child will learn at this stage of their life is descriptive language skills. This refers to the ability to describe an objective, person, experience, or location using written and spoken language.

Guess the Word is a fun game that helps your child develop descriptive language skills by helping them learn how to describe things. The objective is for them to guess what word you are referring to by how you describe it to them. This game also seeks to test and sharpen their listening and comprehension skills. Bear in mind that you may need to describe a word several times and offer plenty of clues to activate your child's memory.

Another trick to help your child guess the word is to use both objective and subjective descriptions. Objective descriptions are facts that cannot change, whereas subjective descriptions are personal thoughts and feelings about the word. Consider the following example of how you would describe a banana using objective and subjective descriptions:

- Objective: It is a fruit that I buy from the grocery store.

- Subjective: I don't like the smell of this fruit.

- Objective: The color of the fruit is yellow.

- Subjective: Daddy loves to cut up the fruit and put it on his sandwiches.

Activity 3: Homophone Pairs

Homophones are words that sound the same but have different spellings and meanings. The best way to explain these types of words to your child is that if they close their eyes and hear the words repeated, they won't be able to tell the difference. For example, "meet" and "meat" sound the same; however, one refers to getting together with someone and the other refers to flesh from an animal.

Homophones are more relevant for written language rather than spoken language. However, they can be a great speech sound exercise to practice with your children. For example, when pairing "Sell" and "Cell," your child learns that the "C" has a soft "S" sound rather than a strong "K" sound like the word "Cat."

To play the game, you will need to have a set of homophone flashcards. These can either be purchased online or made at home. Your flashcards should include pictures for visual aid and the different spelling of words with bold emphasis on similar sounds.

Consider the following examples:

- M-**ee**-t vs. M-**ea**-t
- P-**air**-r vs. P-**ea**-r
- H-**ar**-e vs. H-**ai**-r
- K-**night** vs. **Night**

Activity 4: Character Creation

Help your child practice descriptive language skills by engaging in pretend play. Give them 10 minutes to brainstorm ideas for a fictional character and then ask them questions about their character.

To increase the element of fun, ask your child to find a creative way of introducing their character. For example, they might draw a picture of the character or dress up like them as part of their presentation. Keep the questions that you ask short and open-ended so that your child is encouraged to think and come up with a thoughtful response.

Moreover, the questions you pose should prompt your child to describe various attributes of their character. Here are a few examples:

- What is your character's name?
- Where does your character live?
- What does your character look like?
- What foods does your character enjoy?
- What does your character like to do for fun?

Activity 5: Start a Book Club

When your child was much younger, they got into the habit of listening while you read to them. Now that they are older and have a better grasp of language, you can listen while they practice reading aloud.

For many children, reading aloud is a fear because of the interruptions they might have while reading passages. Starting a book club can be a positive way to encourage your child to read. It is a safe environment where they can refine their speech and language skills without feeling judged by their peers.

Furthermore, what makes book clubs fun is that your child and a few of their friends get to choose which books they are going to read together. The excitement of exploring new fictional worlds with friends makes the experience of reading enjoyable.

Getting your child's full cooperation from the beginning can enhance the success of the book club. Therefore, allow them to choose the name of the club, which friends to invite, and which books to read. If you are going to impose limits, state them upfront. For example, you might limit the size of the book club to four children (including your child) or list book genres that cannot be explored.

Lastly, get parents involved by setting up a group and discussing the finer details of the book club, such as where you are going to meet, how often you will meet, and how to structure the book club to ensure your children get plenty of speech and language training. You may also decide on reading milestones to set for your children and rewards to hand out.

Activity 6: Mad Libs

An ad-lib during a speech or performance is saying words that were not part of the written script. It is a type of improvisation that public speakers, musicians, or actors use to add more depth and quality to their lines.

Mad Libs is a fun and interactive grammar activity that brings silliness to normal ad-libs. The activity aims to present your child with incomplete sentences written in paragraph form. Their task is to read each sentence and figure out which part of speech they can add to complete the sentence. To make the decision-making process easier, you can provide your child with three options and let them choose the best-fitting word.

Here is an example:

My little brother .... a snail for breakfast.

Option 1: Drank

Option 2: Ate

Option 3: Heard

Go through line-by-line looking for the best word to fill the blanks. Use different parts of speech, such as nouns, pronouns, prepositions, verbs, and conjunctions, to expose your child to more grammar. When you have completed all of the sentences, ask your child to read the entire story from the beginning and share laughs about the madness of it!

Activity 7: Comic Strip Creation

Storytelling is a skill that your child will continue to learn as they grow. At this stage of their development, they need to learn how to structure and create storylines for stories. A creative way to reinforce this skill is by creating comic strips with empty speech bubbles. Give your child a few minutes to analyze the pictures and action illustrated so they can come up with suggestions for captions.

Go through each frame and ask your child what they see happening in the frame and what each character is thinking or feeling. Thereafter, hand over a marker and ask them to write text in each speech bubble (you may choose to do the writing, if you like).

When you have filled the speech bubbles for every frame, the real fun begins! Get into your character dress-up costumes and act out the comic strip together. Let your child choose which roles you are going to play and direct the setting and development of the story. Use the speech bubbles as your script for each scene.

Activity 8: Doodle and Describe

Art can be a great way to enhance your child's expressive language. Since the nature of art is highly subjective, there is no right or wrong way for your child to interpret what they think or feel. Toward the end of a long week, you can reward your child by doing an artistic speech and language activity called "Doodle and Describe."

The purpose of the activity is to allow your child the freedom to explore and exercise their creative muscles. The activity is mostly unstructured, meaning your child can decide what type of art to create, which craft supplies to use, and how to structure their time. At the end, you can sit down, view the art created, and ask questions to work on descriptive language. Some questions should elicit objective answers (e.g., what colors did you use?) and others should elicit subjective answers (e.g., how did you feel when you were creating this artwork?)

Activity 9: Guess the Sound

Guess the Sound is a fun game for auditory learners or those who simply love a challenge! The challenge is for your child to see how many sounds they can recognize from an audio recording and write down the correct words on a sheet of paper.

Depending on your child's level of skill, you can either play each sound and pause, allowing them to write down what they hear, or you can play the entire recording and then give them a few minutes to recall all of the sounds they heard (these sounds do not need to be written in the correct order).

The game tests your child's listening, identification, and memory skills. Moreover, it can be a great way to engage their critical thinking skills and increase mental focus. The best time to practice this activity would be in the mornings when your child's brain is most alert or after lunchtime when they get back from school.

Activity 10: Question Chain

Between the ages of 6-8, your child is exposed to more people who are not necessarily close family. For instance, on a normal school day, they interact with their schoolteacher, classmates, school bus driver, traffic controller, or grocery clerks. As a result, social skills become more critical at this stage of their life, as they can assist in building meaningful relationships.

A fun activity to play with your child is called "Question Chain." Start a conversation with a question and ask your child to respond with a question. Continue bouncing back questions until one of you goes blank. This activity teaches your child how to add variety to conversations by showing interest in others. Their listening skills are also tested because they must listen carefully to your question so they can respond with a related question.

Here is an example:

Parent: How was your day?

Child: My day was alright. What about yours?

Parent: Mine went by very fast. What did you learn at school?

Child: We learned about dinosaurs. Did you go to work?

Activity 11: In My Opinion

Young children have a lot to say; however, they need training to articulate their thoughts logically and concisely. It is common for a child with speech or language issues to have difficulty consolidating their ideas and putting them into words. The purpose of this activity is to start showing your child how to do so by taking turns expressing your opinions.

Place a physical object on the table between you and your child. Be the first one to offer an opinion so that your child sees a demonstration of how it should be done. Raise three fingers, indicating three separate points you are going to make. After making each point, drop a finger. It is then your child's turn to offer an opinion about the object and state three points. Instead of using fingers, another option is to say the words "firstly," "secondly," and "thirdly" to show the sequence of your thoughts.

Another way to switch up the activity is to go through a kid-friendly magazine with your child. Find an interesting page and take a few minutes to state your opinions about what you see. Continue to do this until you have completed at least three rounds.

Activity 12: Word-of-the-Day

Vocabulary-building is still an important task for children aged 6-8. For instance, your child may still know fewer words than his or her peers, which makes it difficult for them to read and write.

An exciting activity that the whole family can participate in is having a word of the day. Every morning, around the breakfast table or on the commute to school, share with your children the word for the day. This should be an appropriate word for young children to learn and can be used in everyday speech. Nevertheless, find words that are out of the ordinary or have a rich history behind them to make learning fun.

If you are going to turn this activity into a daily ritual, stay organized by having a list of words with their meanings and pronunciations ready. All you need to do is refer to your list and pick a word you haven't introduced before. To encourage your children to learn the new word, you might challenge them to surprise you by using it in a sentence at any random time during the day.

Activity 13: Artistic Descriptions

Creating art can be turned into a group activity when your child is playing with their siblings or friends. Have the children sit around a table and draw or paint their artwork. When everyone is done, collect the artwork and hand each child someone else's creation. Give the group a few minutes to analyze the drawing or painting and then ask each child to describe what they see.

To guide the children, give them three question prompts to answer:

- Who is in the artwork?

- What action is taking place?

- How does the artwork make you feel?

The original owner of the artwork can offer their opinion at the end. For example, they may want to clarify what the artwork represents or the full storyline behind it. This activity enhances expressive language while also teaching children to empathize and look at situations from other people's perspectives.

Activity 14: Grammar Pop-Up

There are plenty of educational speech therapy apps that can be incorporated into your child's learning program. If you head over to the "App Store" on your smart device and scroll to the education category or type "speech-language games" on the search bar, you will be shown a list of apps to choose from.

You can opt for apps that offer practice for a single or a range of speech and language skills, such as speech development, phonological awareness, vocabulary-building, and language development. Before downloading an app, look at the age restrictions and reviews from other users.

Note that face-to-face interactions are still the ideal choice for speech and language training. However, every once in a while, when you don't have any activities lined up or when you want to switch things up, taking out the tablet and allowing your child to play some games is acceptable.

Here are a few apps recommended:

- **Articulation Station (Paid):** Offers different articulation activities that help your child pronounce, read, and listen to different sounds, sentences, and stories at different levels. This app is perfect for practicing target sounds.

- **Splingo (Paid):** Space-themed app that improves your child's listening and language skills through interactive alien and spaceship games. Designed by SLPs, the app focuses on teaching your child parts of speech at different developmental levels (the advanced level combines multiple aspects of language at once).

- **LAMP (Paid):** This app specifically focuses on developing your child's vocabulary by exposing them to more than 3,000 words and helping them to practice recognizing word patterns and building sentences.

Activity 15: Tongue Twister Challenge

To improve their articulation skills, play a game of tongue twister. Tongue twisters are nonsensical sentences with similar sounding or rhyming words that can enhance your child's speaking skills. The sentences are designed in such a way that they challenge your child to use different mouth and tongue movements.

It is expected for your child to get their tongue in a twist when playing this game, so create a fun and relaxed environment for them to feel free to express themselves. Tongue twisters are intended to be funny and light-hearted too. This is a game that the whole family can get involved with during your bonding time!

Here are a few tongue twisters to try:

- He threw three free throws.

- Sheena leads, Sheila needs.

- A happy hippo hopped and hiccupped.

- Selfish shellfish. (Repeat many times)

- If a dog chews shoes, whose shoes does he choose?

Activity 16: Echo Game

Imitation is a tool used in speech therapy to improve children's receptive language skills. Receptive language refers to what children hear and how they interpret the information. A fun activity to enhance your child's receptive language skills is the Echo Game.

Sit facing your child and make eye contact. Tell them to maintain eye contact throughout the game so that they can imitate what you do or say. For instance, you might say a simple sentence in an angry voice using a strong facial expression. Immediately afterward, your child has to imitate your actions and words. Start at a slow pace with basic sentences and actions. As your child picks up on the pattern, create longer sentences and complex actions (e.g., going from a sad to a happy tone of voice).

If there is enough time, switch roles and allow your child to lead the game. Take directions from them based on their actions and words. It is okay for both of you to break out of character and make silly sounds or faces. This is part of what makes the Echo Game fun!

Activity 17: Vocabulary Charades

Charades is a versatile, multi-generational game suitable for young children, adults, and groups. The game tests your ability to describe a word or experience by miming or making gestures. Other participants need to guess what word is being acted out.

Vocabulary charades adds a twist to the traditional game and makes the activity fun for your little one. One person chooses a flashcard with a word that your child is familiar with and acts out the word without talking. Everyone else participating must guess what the word is. The person who guesses the correct word gets to choose a new flashcard and stand in front.

This game can be played with family members or with your child's peers. The vocabulary chosen can also be based on themes, such as "vacation," "animals," or "occupations" to make it easier for your child to recognize and recall the correct word.

Activity 18: Word Construction Site

Have you ever seen a construction site? There are piles of building materials stacked in different areas that are used by builders to construct the building. When you look at each building material separately, you don't quite get the full picture of what the final product will look like.

Word Construction Site helps your child construct words out of separate prefixes, suffixes, and root cards laying across the floor. Similar to constructing a building, their job is to go through the pile and build words. This continues until there are no more word-building materials on the floor.

The best way to prepare for this activity is to create your own prefix, suffix, and root cards using cardboard paper squares and a black marker (optional: Laminate the cards to prevent wear and tear).

Example of prefixes:

- Ex-

- In-

- Pre-

- Pro-

- Co-
- Re-
- Sub-
- De-
- Mis-
- Be-

Example of suffixes:

- -ful
- -ness
- -ment
- -age
- -ery
- -tion
- -ity
- -ant
- -ing
- -er

Example of root words:

- -act-
- -form-
- -kind-
- -build-
- -fear-

- -friend-

- -like-

- -honest-

- -view-

- -sleep-

Activity 19: Adjective Search

Adjectives are describing words that are useful in building sentences and creating rich and meaningful conversations. Help your child expand their mental inventory of adjectives by memorizing different ways to describe objects, people, and experiences.

On days when your child has a lot of energy, have them run around the house playing a game of Adjective Search. Give them a target word to focus on, like "beautiful" or "small," and have them bring you three items that fit the description. You may want to restrict the game to the playroom to regulate what items your child grabs!

To increase the difficulty of the game, give your child two target words to focus on. In other words, the items they find must fit two descriptions (e.g., a small and beautiful doll). Add a third descriptive word for an even greater challenger!

Activity 20: Pen Pal Letter

It is important to balance practicing verbal communication with written communication. The general belief is that your child speaks as well as they write and writes as well as they speak. A fun and social way to encourage your child to practice writing skills is to get them to write pen pal letters to friends or cousins in different states or countries. A few skills are reinforced through this exercise, namely:

- developing social skills

- building empathy

- perspective-taking

- starting and continuing conversations

- grammar and language skills

If you cannot find a suitable pen pal for your child, have them write letters to themselves. These can take the form of journal entries and can be based on any idea or topic your child wishes to explore deeper. Journal prompts for children are also useful in teaching your child how to write stories and structure their ideas on a specific topic.

Here are some recommended journal prompts:

- Favorite book

- Describe your perfect day.

- What makes you smile?

- Favorite place

- What makes a good friend?

- Who is your hero and why?

- What makes you special?

- Favorite movie

- What makes you afraid?

- Favorite subject at school

Chapter 8:

Speech Games and Activities

for Children Aged 9-13

*You cannot make people learn. You can only provide the right conditions
for learning to happen.*
—Vince Gowmon

What Speech Therapy for Children Aged 9-13 Looks Like

Speech therapy is not strictly for young children. It is an effective treatment for middle schoolers, high schoolers, and adults too. Between the ages of 9-13, your child recognizes plenty of common words, even though they may still need to get a firm grasp of grammar and language skills.

Unless they are living with a chronic speech or language disorder, they can speak like other children their age and contribute to conversations around common topics. However, due to their early childhood speech delays, your child may struggle to clearly express their ideas. This error needs to be corrected ideally before they become teenagers so they can walk into adolescence being able to express needs and wants, organize their thoughts and present them logically, and feel comfortable sharing views in front of others.

The following activities are designed to equip your child with the communication tools to confidently express who they are and enhance the quality of their relationships. Speech and language skills will be presented at an advanced level since your child already has the basic foundation formed.

20 Fun and Interactive Speech-Language Games and Activities

Complete the following activities in the order you prefer. Since you know your child best, you are welcome to personalize any of these activities to match their interests and preferences. Remember that while instructions are important to follow, your child has the freedom to interpret these activities however they like.

Lastly, have fun teaching and guiding your child along this journey!

Activity 1: Wh- Questions Game

Wh- questions, like who, what, when, where, and why, are commonly used to understand the context of a situation and expand on ideas and concepts. Learning how to answer these questions can help your child demonstrate their knowledge on a topic and provide richer and more specific responses.

There are several reasons why your child might struggle to respond to Wh- questions. One reason is that they don't understand the word and therefore don't know how to provide the best response (e.g., not knowing that "when?" is a time-based question). Another reason is they don't understand the grammatical structure of the question.

To help your child understand and use Wh- questions more often, you can play the Wh- Question Game. Choose an age-appropriate TV show that your child is not familiar with (e.g., a small-town or college-based series). Let your child know beforehand that you are watching the show for educational purposes and will ask them Wh- questions every five minutes.

This activity works well if you have already watched the episode and can create great questions to test your child's comprehension skills and ability to answer questions about the show. At the back of your question paper, have the correct answers written down so you can discuss them with your child afterward.

Activity 2: Wishlist Creation

Effective communication involves the exchange of ideas. These ideas are what carry meaning and make the messages being transferred worthwhile. It is important to teach your child how to communicate with purpose by having clear intentions about what they want to say and why they want to say it.

Finding the "why?" behind a message can be difficult for children because it requires them to reflect on their ideas, beliefs, and feelings, and formulate a strong argument or opinion. This difficulty explains why some children will respond with "because" when asked why they think or feel a certain way.

Nevertheless, your child is reaching a stage of their life where they will need to develop critical thinking skills. You can help them develop these skills by practicing activities like Wishlist Creation. Ask your child to go to an online store they frequently purchase from and fill up their wishlist cart with essential items they need (you can impose a budget to make the exercise a little more difficult).

When they have found their essentials, get them to explain why they have chosen each item. The idea, belief, or feeling behind their choice must be clear for them to win a round. Items that don't have a clear "why?" get disqualified (removed from the wishlist cart). You can decide how to reward your child for making solid arguments. For example, you may decide to purchase a few or all of the items they were able to convince you about.

Activity 3: My Role Model

Every child has a role model. Do you know who your child's role model is? To sharpen your child's grammar, sentence construction, and storytelling skills, ask them to reflect on somebody whom they admire and present to them. How your child decides to design their presentation is up to them. For example, they may write a speech, record a video, or design a PowerPoint presentation.

The presentation must provide a brief background on the individual, the strengths or talents that make them exceptional, and the significance they have on your child's life (the deeper "why?").

Since your child is much older and may need a bigger incentive to complete this activity, offer them a reward for making the effort. For example, if their role model is a basketball player, you might offer them tickets to the next basketball game or buy a t-shirt with their number. You can also invite close family members to listen to form an audience and listen to your child's presentation!

Activity 4: Pros and Cons

Perspective-taking is an advanced language skill that your child is old enough to start developing. It can be defined as the ability to see all sides of an argument. Most times, your child understands information from their perspective. This is important; however, they must be able to switch sides and see things from another perspective too.

To practice perspective-taking, place a deck of cards with general topics written on them. Flip over the first card and ask your child to state the pros and cons of the scenario described on the card. For example, if the card says "Homeschooling," ask them to either write down or speak about the pros and cons of homeschooling.

This activity requires some preparation. For example, you will need to create your cards using rectangular-shaped cardboard paper and a marker to write (optional: Laminate the paper to prevent wear and tear). It may be useful to also have a cheat sheet prepared with a list of pros and cons for each card. This cheat sheet can help you suggest a few pros and cons to your child, which they can expand on.

Activity 5: News Report

Role-playing with an older child looks slightly different from role-playing with a younger one. While the intention is still the same—to encourage them to think out of the box—the scenarios suggested reflect the life of a much older individual. One way to practice role-playing and practice speaking skills is to ask your child to pretend they are a news reporter. Allow them to pick a funny or serious topic they would like to report on, such as the long bus queue in the mornings or an environmental issue.

To make this game fun, give your child props, costumes, and accessories to wear. You can even create a television set with a cardboard cut-out and have them sit on the other side. You could be the producer holding a video camera and capturing the moment!

Activity 6: Mind Mapping

Children with fluency disorder are known to have difficulty speaking without interruptions. One of the causes of these interruptions is the speed at which their minds process information. In essence, they have plenty of great ideas but struggle to slow down their minds, collect their thoughts, and present coherent and logical thoughts.

If your child has this type of speech issue, mind mapping can help them organize their ideas on a page, make connections between similar words and ideas, and make sense of the information. Encourage your child to complete a mind map when preparing for speeches or presentations to identify key topics or themes to explore. They can also use mind maps to brainstorm conversation topics if they are preparing to meet new people and want to practice different conversation starters.

Lastly, mind maps are useful for taking down notes in class. Since the tool promotes the use of keywords, your child can spend a few seconds or minutes writing down the main ideas, and then summarize what they learned in class at home.

Activity 7: Social Cue Tracker

It is common for a child with speech and language difficulties to also have problems with picking up on social cues. This may be caused by a co-occurring condition like ASD or simply the inability to pick up on nuances in language and appropriate social behaviors.

It can be embarrassing for your child to find themselves as the "butt of someone's joke" because they misinterpreted what they meant by using a certain tone of voice, phrase, or expression. Thus, to prevent this from happening, you can help them create a Social Cue Tracker using a notebook or journal. This is simply a list, in table format, of social cues, along with their meanings, and when they are typically seen. Every time your child learns about a new social cue, get them to add it to their list.

Here is an example:

Social cue	Meaning	When is it typically seen?
Someone looks away when you are speaking to them	The person may be disengaged or uncomfortable.	When sensitive topics are brought up or when the speaker talks for too long without giving the other person a chance.

Activity 8: DESO Technique

The DESO technique is a communication tool used to practice expressing needs and setting boundaries assertively. The word "DESO" is an acronym that stands for:

- **Describe:** Objectively state what is happening or has recently happened that you didn't appreciate.

- **Express:** Describe how the situation made you feel using "I" statements.

- **Specify:** Be clear about what actions you need to see moving forward.

- **Outcome:** Explain the consequences of not fulfilling your needs or repeating the same violation in the future.

Here is an example of how your child might use the DESO technique:

Describe: Maddy, yesterday in class, you laughed at me when I was trying to explain my point.

Express: I felt embarrassed because everyone was watching me.

Specify: Please do not laugh or make jokes when I am sharing my opinions.

Outcome: If you continue, I will report your behavior to the teacher.

Go through different scenarios with your child and use the DESO technique to help them practice expressing their needs and setting boundaries.

Activity 9: Validating Behaviors

Validating someone is the act of acknowledging what they are saying with words or body language. For example, saying, "I understand what you are saying," or maintaining eye contact during a conversation are both examples of validating behaviors. Teaching your child how to validate others during conversations can enhance their listening and comprehension skills. This is because they are encouraged to focus on the intent behind another person's message and understand where they are coming from.

When teaching your child validating behaviors, make use of role-playing. For example, one of you might be a patient and the other person a doctor. The patient might express different concerns and the doctor's job is to offer validation. Other role-playing scenarios that can work are teacher-student, parent-child, and boss-employee.

It is also important to expose your child to different validation techniques. For example, one way to validate someone is to show empathy. This can be expressed through phrases like:

- "I hear what you are saying."

- "I know how difficult this is for you."

- "I can imagine how you are feeling."

Another way to validate someone is by paraphrasing what they have said. Listening is essential when choosing this technique because your child will need to process the whole message and briefly summarize what they heard. Here are a few opening lines they can use when paraphrasing:

- "It sounds like you are saying..."

- "What I get from your message is..."

- "Are you saying that..."

Validation doesn't always need to be communicated with words. Sometimes, it can be expressed through facial expressions and body language. Practice validating non-verbal communication with your child like nodding, smiling, and maintaining eye contact.

Activity 10: Learning Reflection

Teach your child to have a positive attitude when receiving constructive feedback by showing them how to self-reflect on their work. An important message to emphasize is that not all feedback is negative. Being corrected and shown how to improve is essential for learning and growth.

There are some situations, specifically in the classroom environment, that warrant feedback. These include:

- Receiving feedback after a class test

- Being given pointers after a speech or presentation

- When being reprimanded for inappropriate behaviors

Teach your child to reflect when receiving constructive feedback. Learning reflection means asking open-ended questions about how they might improve going forward. Instead of assuming the feedback is negative, encourage them to find positive pointers to improve their behaviors or performance.

Here are some learning reflection questions your child can answer after receiving feedback:

- What were the important ideas shared during the feedback session?

- What valuable advice or suggestions did you receive?

- What was difficult to accept or understand about the feedback?

- What new habits do you need to develop to improve your behaviors or performance?

- Who can help you when you get stuck and need support?

Activity 11: Story Retelling

At the middle-school level, your child is expected to display advanced language skills like summarizing information. This may seem like a simple task for you and me, but it isn't for someone who grew up with speech and language delays. For example, to summarize an article, the following skills are tested:

- comprehension skills

- working memory (i.e., remembering details)

- categorization skills

- sequencing

- paraphrasing

- filtering necessary and unnecessary details

- constructing clear and logical sentences

Teaching your child how to summarize information at this level will prepare them for later grades when this skill will become significantly important across academic subjects. A fun and interactive activity to reinforce summarization is Story Retelling. The aim is for your child to listen to a short story or news article and summarize what they heard using their own words.

To make it easier for them, include an aspect of role-playing. For instance, you might ask your child to pretend they are shopping at a grocery store when, suddenly, they see an individual shoplifting. Add a few more details to the story and add some characters like a store clerk and a police officer. Then, ask your child to retell the events that transpired at the grocery store using their own words.

Activity 12: Record and Review Conversations

Another aspect of speech and language is voice control. When your child has command over their voice, they can pronounce words, pause at the right place, and manage the sound and projection of their voice.

If you always find yourself asking your child to speak louder or softer, articulate their words, or pace themselves when they are talking, they can benefit from practicing a voice exercise like Record and Review Conversations.

Sit in a quiet room with your child and record them while they read a short story. Playback the recording for them and encourage them to identify areas of improvement. Exchange ideas and feedback openly and demonstrate what they should be doing. For example, you might show them an example of pausing when they see a comma or full stop. Repeat the exercise and compare the difference between the first and second recordings.

This exercise can be helpful before the day of a school speech or presentation. It is also a positive exercise to practice the day before your child attends a social gathering to help them lower social anxiety.

Activity 13: Two Truths and a Lie

An exciting group activity to play with your child and a few of their close friends is called "Two Truths and a Lie." The rules of this game are simple: Each participant has a turn telling the rest of the group two truths and a lie. These should be facts about their personal life that other participants may not know. The challenge is for the group to guess which facts are true and false.

While this game is fun and competitive, it is an effective way to practice articulation skills and non-verbal communication. The goal is to state each fact as clearly and fluently as possible without any pauses or interruptions so that participants struggle to detect the lie. Your child also needs to mask their emotions and practice speaking in a neutral voice.

Activity 14: I Feel/I Need

As your child approaches puberty, it is normal for them to start feeling sudden bouts of strong emotions. Their body is growing through several changes and hormonal imbalances are common during this time. Nevertheless, they need to learn emotional regulation skills to manage triggers, de-escalate conflict, and communicate their needs.

A simple sentence to teach your child is the "I feel...I need" sentence. Whenever they start to feel overwhelmed, they can take a moment to pause and reflect on what they are feeling at the moment and what they need to feel better. Doing this allows them to take ownership of their experiences and respond to their own needs.

For example, if your child feels stressed about an upcoming school test, they might approach the subject teacher and say, "I feel nervous about the upcoming test. I need more practice papers to work on." Or if they are frustrated by their younger siblings invading their privacy, they might approach you and say, "I feel irritated when Simon plays in my room. I need time for myself."

Go through a few more scenarios with your child to teach them various ways of using this simple, yet effective, sentence.

Activity 15: Read, Recap, Relate

Read, Recap, Relate is a summarization activity with a twist. It encourages your child to not only summarize what they have understood but to also relate it to their personal experiences. The first step is for them to read the story out loud. They can do this as many times as it takes to understand the context and details of what they are reading.

The second step is for them to summarize what they have read, extracting the main idea and points of the story or article. Finally, the third step is for them to relate what they read to a real-life experience. This teaches them how to read between the lines and make connections between ideas. Moreover, your child can practice personalizing information and providing their own opinions.

When picking stories or articles for them to read, choose topics or genres that they are interested in. For example, you might find an article about a musician they listen to or an article speaking about the value of friendship. Make sure there is enough information in the story that can resonate with your child so that they have enough content to form a strong opinion.

Activity 16: Fill the Silence

A common fear for young people is running out of things to say during impromptu conversations. For some, this fear can be so great that they avoid speaking to new people or in group settings.

Help your child overcome this fear by playing a game of Fill the Silence. Engage in a casual back-and-forth conversation with them, then spontaneously stop speaking. The challenge is for your child to fill the silence by picking up the conversation and prompting you to speak again. Repeat this several times and keep your child guessing when the next silent moment will be. Not only are you testing their conversational skills, but you are also sharpening their listening and concentration.

Before starting the game, make a few suggestions on how your child can fill the silence. For example, they can ask a question related to the last thing you said, share a personal opinion, or raise a new topic of discussion. The better your child gets at this game, the less time it will take them to think on their feet and fill the silences in conversation.

Activity 17: Gratitude Journal

Speech and language development takes a lot of time and patience to master. There will be times when your child speaks with clarity and confidence and other times when they forget the rules they have been taught. Through the highs and lows, your child needs to maintain a sense of competence so they feel motivated to stay open-minded and curious. A gratitude journal can be a great tool to remind them of their progress and keep their spirits high!

Journaling is an effective exercise to help your child refine their speech and language skills. It teaches them grammatical structure, storytelling techniques, and new vocabulary. Other non-literacy-related skills reinforced through journaling are self-awareness and emotional intelligence.

A gratitude journal is a notebook dedicated to documenting your child's strengths, accomplishments, positive memories, lessons learned, and praise received from others. In essence, anything that can inspire them to keep going can be recorded in their gratitude journal.

Challenge your child to write in their gratitude journal often, such as whenever they make progress at school, reach a personal milestone, or need something to boost their self-confidence. You can purchase a gratitude journal for kids with prompts included or suggest the following prompts to get them started:

- What are you thankful for?

- What made you smile recently?

- What's the best thing that happened today?

- What interesting fact have you recently learned at school?

- Name and describe someone who has shown you kindness recently.

- Who are your favorite teachers, and why?

- Describe a funny conversation you recently had.

- What is something new that you have learned about yourself?

- What are your favorite words right now, and why?

- What are you enjoying most about improving your speaking skills?

Activity 18: Slow Motion

Enunciation is the ability to pronounce every sound of a word. Children who often mumble their words need to practice slowing their pace and pronouncing every sound. If your child is struggling with this issue, you can play a game of Slow Motion. Get your child to repeat a long sentence twice: The first time fast or normal speaking pace, and the second time very slowly, moving their mouth in slow motion.

Speaking this slowly is not natural; however, it is a great way to help them learn how to pace themselves and their words. If your child isn't able to slow down their speaking pace, ask them to place the knuckle of the thumb inside their mouth and repeat the sentence normally. Having something in their mouth may force them to be more intentional about articulating each word.

Activity 19: Mirror Exercises

A great way to enhance your child's awareness about how they speak is to put them in front of a mirror and ask them to observe their lip, teeth, and tongue movements when talking. You may decide to stand next to them and model the correct movements when making certain sounds.

There are so many other communication skills that your child can practice while looking into a mirror. For example, they can practice making appropriate facial expressions and body language or changing their tone of voice when conveying certain messages. These exercises promote higher self-esteem and self-awareness, which are essential when interacting with others.

Activity 20: Thought Groups

Pausing often when sharing ideas or information is an advanced speech and language skill. It requires your child to know the right moments in a sentence to take a brief pause. Punctuation marks can assist your child with this. For example, they can learn to pause when they see a comma or full stop. However, text may not always include punctuation marks to help them.

Recognizing thought groups within sentences is an effective way to recognize the right moments to pause when punctuation is not included. Thought groups are simply big ideas that deserve a moment of reflection afterward so that listeners can process and make sense of the information. They often answer at least one Wh- question: What, where, when, who, or why.

Short sentences have fewer thought groups than longer sentences and therefore will contain fewer pauses. For example, the following sentence contains one thought group   and answers the question "What?" Thus, it doesn't require a pause in between words.

/I ate ice cream for breakfast/

The next example contains two thought groups and answers two questions: "When?" and "What?" It, therefore, requires a pause between the two thought groups.

/Tomorrow/I will eat ice cream for breakfast/

The last example contains three thought groups and answers three questions: "When?" "What?" and "Who?" It, therefore, requires two pauses between the three thought groups.

/Tomorrow/I will eat ice cream for breakfast/with my two friends Sam and Tony/

Knowing when to pause will be much easier once your child starts recognizing thought groups. Go through short stories and articles and practice identifying the right moments to pause when reading.

Bonus Chapter:

Speech Therapy Passages

The best teachers are those who show you where to look, but don't tell you what to see.
—Alexandra K. Trenfor

Target Sound Passages to Practice at Home

Practicing target sounds in isolation can help you correct mispronunciation of sounds immediately and give your child plenty of practice to get it right. The following target sound passages are designed for children between the ages of 5-10 who are still learning articulation skills. The passages also include questions to test your child's listening and comprehension skills.

Passage 1: "Danny's Deep Blue Eyes" (D Sound)

Danny is a delightful girl with deep blue eyes. During the day, her blue eyes twinkle in the sun. In the evening, they turn into a darker shade of blue. "Why are your eyes so blue, Danny?" asked her friend. "I don't know," responded Danny; "You need to ask my Mom or Dad.

Questions:

1. What color are Danny's eyes?
2. What happens to Danny's eyes in the evening?
3. Who asked Danny why her eyes were so blue?

Passage 2: "Cooking in the Kitchen" (K Sound)

Katie found her Mom cooking in the kitchen and asked, "What are you making Mom?" Her mom took the bowl on the counter and showed Katie what she was making. It was Katie's favorite dessert: Chocolate chip cookies. "Can I help you?" Katie asked with a smile. "Yes, of course you can," said Katie's Mom. Grab a stool and come join me!

Questions:

1. Where did Katie find her Mom?
2. What dessert was Katie's Mom making?

3. What object did Katie's Mom tell her to grab?

Passage 3: "The Funny School Photo" (F Sound)

It was Photo Day at school and Miss Daphney called the class to the front of the classroom. "Let us stand in a row and smile at the camera," she said cheerfully. All of the students followed the instructions, except for Fiona. She looked at the camera and made a silly face. "Fiona," said Miss Daphney, "Stop fooling around!" The other students thought Fiona's silly face was funny and they laughed out loud.

Questions:

1. Where did Miss Daphney call the students?

2. What instruction did Miss Daphney give to the students?

3. What did Fiona do when she looked into the camera?

Passage 4: "Sammy's Big Secret" (S Sound)

Sammy kept a big secret from his Mom and Dad. The only person who knew about the secret was his sister. One morning, before school, Sammy decided it was time to share his big secret with his parents. "Mom and Dad," he said trembling, "The dog ate my homework." His parents looked at him with a smile and said, "Yes, we know Sammy. We saw the dog running away with your papers!"

Questions:

1. What was Sammy's big secret?

2. Who else knew about the secret before telling his parents?

3. What time of day did Sammy decide to share his big secret?

Passage 5: "The Naughty Knight" (N Sound)

Once upon a time, there was a naughty knight who never knew how to fight. Whenever the King called him to battle, he would say, "Not today; my neck is sore, and I need to rest." One day, the King returned early from the battleground and found the knight dancing in the courtyard. "Didn't you say your neck was sore?" said the King angrily. The naughty knight promised that day to never lie again.

Questions:

1. What challenge did the naughty knight have?

2. What did the naughty knight lie to the King and say?

3. What activity did the King find the naughty knight doing in the courtyard?

Conclusion

We see how early childhood experiences are so important to lifelong outcomes, how the early environment becomes embedded in the brain and changes its architecture.
—Andrew S. Garner

Children may go through similar stages of life and learn the same sets of skills, but every child is unique and paves their journey in the world. As a parent of a child with speech delays, it is important to remember that a delay is not a denial. Your child is still capable of developing speech and language skills but may choose to do it at their own pace and schedule.

Many parents often refer to developmental milestones to assess whether children are growing as expected. However, slow development is still considered normal. There is never a time when you should panic about your child's development because even if they are showing signs of other underlying conditions, there are professional medical doctors available to hold your hand and walk the path of recovery with you and your family.

One of the most important doctors you will come across on your path is a speech-language pathologist (SLP). They are the ones who will conduct a thorough assessment of your child and determine whether they have a speech or language disorder, or both. They can also pick up on co-occurring conditions like autism, hearing loss, oral-motor problems, and cognitive disabilities. By the time you walk out of their office, you will know with certainty what challenges your child is facing and the best interventions to start immediately.

The purpose of this book was to introduce you to a popular intervention used to treat speech delays and disorders called speech therapy. The goal of speech therapy is to help your child develop the necessary speech and language skills to pronounce sounds and words, expand their vocabulary, learn how to build sentences and enhance their reading and writing abilities. Even though speech therapy is traditionally administered by an SLP in a regulated therapy room, you can reinforce skills taught during speech therapy sessions at home.

The good news is that you can significantly improve your child's speaking abilities by turning your home into an additional learning environment for your child. This means that instead of waiting for their weekly speech therapy session to get speech and language training, they can practice at home, on a daily basis, with you, or on their own.

With that said, there is a lot of preparation and planning that must go into cultivating a learning environment for your child at home. Many of these strategies were provided in the book and included things like adopting a play-based learning approach, modifying your parenting style to promote competence, engagement, and inclusivity, and creating a program that includes specific goals and caters to your child's needs.

The best part about this book, however, is the section on games and activities to practice with your child at each stage of their development (as well as the bonus chapter offering practice for target sounds). As already mentioned, you are welcome to customize these games and activities to match your child's interests and needs, thereby increasing the success rate. If you are ever worried about running out of speech exercises at home, now you have 60 fun and diverse games and activities to choose from!

This comprehensive speech therapy guide has provided you with all of the tools required to give your child the best start in life. The type of behaviors you model at home, the positive interactions you have with your child, and the nurturing learning environment you create can all work to encourage your little one or older child to become an effective communicator.

All that's left is for you to take a courageous first step and embark on this remarkable journey to help your late talker develop the skills to confidently express themselves!

If this book has provided you with sufficient knowledge and tools to take a proactive approach in addressing your child's speech delays, please leave a review on the Amazon page!

About the Author

Richard Bass is a well-established author with extensive knowledge and background on children's disabilities. Richard has also experienced first-hand many children and teens who deal with depression and anxiety. He enjoys researching techniques and ideas to better serve students, as well as guiding parents on how to understand and lead their children to success.

Richard wants to share his experience, research, and practices through his writing, as it has proven successful for many parents and students.

Richard feels there is a need for parents and others around the child to fully understand the disability or the mental health of the child. He hopes that with his writing, people will be more understanding of children going through these issues.

Richard Bass has been in education for over a decade and holds a bachelor's and master's degree in education as well as several certifications including Special Education K-12, and Educational Administration.

Whenever Richard is not working, reading, or writing he likes to travel with his family to learn about different cultures as well as get ideas from all around about the upbringing of children, especially those with disabilities. Richard also researches and learns about different educational systems around the world.

Richard participates in several online groups where parents, educators, doctors, and psychologists share their success with children with disabilities. Richard is in the process of growing a Facebook group where further discussion about his books and techniques could take place. Apart from online groups, he has also attended trainings regarding the upbringing of students with disabilities and has also led trainings in this area.

A Message from the Author

If you enjoyed the book and are interested on further updates or just a place to share your thoughts with other readers or myself, please join my Facebook group by scanning below!

If you would be interested on receiving a FREE Planner for kids PDF version, by signing up you will also receive exclusive notifications to when new content is released and will be able to receive it at a promotional price. Scan below to sign up!

Scan below to check out my content on You Tube and learn more about Neurodiversity!

References

5 ABA principles that speech and language therapists use. (2017, July 31). ABA Connect. https://abaconnect.co.uk/2017/07/31/5-aba-principles-that-speech-and-language-therapists-use/

5 common components of ABA therapy for children with ASD. (2020, September 9). Lumiere Children's Therapy. https://www.lumierechild.com/lumiere-childrens-therapy/5-common-components-of-aba-therapy-for-children-with-asd

11 positive parenting strategies you need to start using. (2020, November 6). ProdigyGame. https://www.prodigygame.com/main-en/blog/positive-parenting/

ABA and speech therapy: Comparing two therapeutic concepts. (2019, December 3). Regis College. https://online.regiscollege.edu/blog/aba-and-speech-therapy/#:~:text=ABA%20therapists%20can%20also%20learn

ACECQA. (2019, June 13). *The importance of play in children's learning and development.* StartingBlocks. https://www.startingblocks.gov.au/other-resources/factsheets/the-importance-of-play-in-children-s-learning-and-development

ASHA. (2009). *Activities to encourage speech and language development.* Asha. https://www.asha.org/public/speech/development/Activities-to-Encourage-Speech-and-Language-Development/

Barnes, A. (2022, February 1). *Why teenagers receive speech therapy and how it works.* Expressable. https://www.expressable.com/learning-center/tips-and-resources/why-teenagers-receive-speech-therapy-and-how-it-works

Bauby, J.-D. (2019). *Jean-Dominique Bauby quote*. Goodreads. https://www.goodreads.com/author/show/75287.Jean_Do minique_Bauby

Benefits of routine. (2020, June 8). Charlotte Speech and Hearing Center. https://charlottespeechhearing.com/benefits-of-routine/

Beurkens, N. (2016, September 21). *The key to competent children: Build self-esteem, reduce resistance, instill responsibility*. Nicole Beurkens. https://www.drbeurkens.com/competence-key-improving-self-esteem-reducing-resistance-instilling-responsibility-promoting-positive-mood-children/

Bradley, S. (2023, February 28). *The 9 best speech therapy apps of 2022*. Verywell Family. https://www.verywellfamily.com/best-speech-therapy-apps-4707573

Breglia, E. (2021, July 19). *What is play-based speech therapy?* Mable Therapy. https://www.mabletherapy.com/blog/2021/07/19/play-based-speech-therapy-what-is-it-and-what-are-the-benefits

Broomfield, J., & Dodd, B. (2011). Is speech and language therapy effective for children with primary speech and language impairment? Report of a randomized control trial. *International Journal of Language & Communication Disorders*, *46*(6), 628–640. https://doi.org/10.1111/j.1460-6984.2011.00039.x

Byjus. (n.d.). *75 tongue twisters in english*. BYJUS. https://byjus.com/english/tongue-twisters/

CDC. (2018, October 22). *Important milestones: Your baby by two months*. Centers for Disease Control and Prevention. https://www.cdc.gov/ncbddd/actearly/milestones/mileston es-2mo.html

CHAMP. (2022, September 6). *Validation: Show you're listening—even if you disagree.* HPRC. https://www.hprc-online.org/social-fitness/relationship-building/validation-show-youre-listening-even-if-you-disagree

Cleveland Clinic. (n.d.). *Articulation disorder: What it is, types & treatment.* Cleveland Clinic. https://my.clevelandclinic.org/health/diseases/23454-articulation-disorder

Cleveland Clinic. (2023a). *Developmental delays.* Cleveland Clinic. https://my.clevelandclinic.org/health/diseases/14814-developmental-delay-in-children

Cleveland Clinic. (2023b). *Speech therapy: What is it? Types, tests & treatment.* Cleveland Clinic. https://my.clevelandclinic.org/health/treatments/22366-speech-therapy

Cloyd, K. (2020, October 15). *My child has A speech delay and asd–here's our story.* Scary Mommy. https://www.scarymommy.com/raising-child-with-speech-delay

Crouse, S. (2022, September 14). *How to use bingo in speech therapy.* Stacy Crouse. https://www.stacycrouse.com/post/bingo-speech-therapy

Dalziel, A. (2023, June 9). *Benefits of play in speech therapy.* Anna Dee SLP. https://www.annadeeslp.com/post/benefits-of-play-in-speech-therapy

Dean, J. (n.d.). *Best speech therapy quotes.* TheraPlatform. https://www.theraplatform.com/blog/961/best-speech-therapy-quotes

Dehaze, A. (n.d.). *"Nurturing an inclusive culture begins in the family. Home is the first place to foster openness and a culture of inclusion." —Alain Dehaze.* The Foundation for a Better Life.

https://www.passiton.com/inspirational-quotes/7968-nurturing-an-inclusive-culture-begins-in-the

Development delay vs disability; there is a difference. (2022, August 31). Script Type Publishing. https://www.scriptype.com/2022/08/31/three-best-ways-to-interact-with-people-with-disabilities-2/#:~:text=Children%20may%20outgrow%20or%20catch

Emma. (2013, December 27). *Taking turns: how to make it easier for your child with special needs.* FriendshipCircle. https://www.friendshipcircle.org/blog/2011/10/25/taking-turns-how-to-make-it-easier-for-your-child-with-special-needs

Garner, A. S. (2019, May 29). *Inspiring quotes on child learning and development.* Vince Gowmon. https://www.vincegowmon.com/inspiring-quotes-on-child-learning-and-development/

Geller, A. (n.d.). *Speech therapy for a 3-year-old: How to get started.* Connected Speech Pathology. https://connectedspeechpathology.com/blog/speech-therapy-for-a-3-year-old

Gowmon, V. (2019, May 29). *Inspiring quotes on child learning and development.* Vince Gowmon. https://www.vincegowmon.com/inspiring-quotes-on-child-learning-and-development/

Gowrie Marketing. (n.d.). *What is play based learning?* Gowrie NSW. https://www.gowriensw.com.au/blog/what-is-play-based-learning

Great Speech. (2021, September 30). *6-Year-Old speech milestones - literacy and reading skills - concept development.* Great Speech. https://greatspeech.com/6-year-old-speech-milestones/#:~:text=Most%206%2Dyear%2Dolds%20are

Great Speech. (2023, February 28). *What is the success rate of speech therapy?* Great Speech. https://greatspeech.com/what-is-the-success-rate-of-speech-therapy/

Gregory, L. (2022, November 10). *Redirecting behavior: How to deal with challenging behavior.* MyBrightWheel. https://mybrightwheel.com/blog/redirecting-behavior

Hartnett, J. K. (2019). *Speech-Language therapy (for parents).* KidsHealth. https://kidshealth.org/en/parents/speech-therapy.html

How to use puppets in speech therapy. (2013, December 2). Super Power Speech. https://superpowerspeech.com/2013/12/i-heart-puppets.html#:~:text=Use%20puppets%20to%20demonstr ate%20how

Irazoque, A. (2023, May 16). *What are phonological disorders, and how are they treated?* Expressable. https://www.expressable.com/learning-center/speech-and-language-issues/what-are-phonological-disorders-and-how-are-they-treated

Janelle. (2023, September 25). *Creating an effective play based learning environment.* My Teaching Cupboard. https://www.myteachingcupboard.com/blog/play-based-learning-environment

Karen. (2023, July 6). *20 best speech therapy apps for preschool (free and paid).* The Pedi Speechie. https://thepedispeechie.com/2023/07/20-best-speech-therapy-apps-for-preschool-free-and-paid.html

Keffer, S. (n.d.). *Did I cause my child's speech delay?* Toddler Talk. https://toddlertalk.com/blog/did-i-cause-my-childs-speech-delay

KidSense. (2011, May 6). *Speech sounds development chart .* Kid Sense Child Development. https://childdevelopment.com.au/resources/child-development-charts/speech-sounds-developmental-chart/

Knost, L. (2019, May 29). *Inspiring quotes on child learning and development.* Vince Gowmon. https://www.vincegowmon.com/inspiring-quotes-on-child-learning-and-development/

Larrazabal, M. (2022, October 28). *Stuttering and typical disfluency: How to differentiate.* Better Speech. https://www.betterspeech.com/post/stuttering-and-typical-disfluency-how-to-differentiate

Law, F., Mahr, T., Schneeberg, A., & Edwards, J. (2016). Vocabulary size and auditory word recognition in preschool children. *Applied Psycholinguistics, 38*(1), 89–125. https://doi.org/10.1017/s0142716416000126

Lee, K. (2021, July 31). *Keep tone and words positive when communicating with your child.* Verywell Family. https://www.verywellfamily.com/how-do-you-talk-to-your-child-620058

Marine, J. (n.d.). *Best speech therapy quotes.* TheraPlatform. https://www.theraplatform.com/blog/961/best-speech-therapy-quotes

Mcilroy, T. (2021, June 14). *Sequencing for preschoolers: Simple ways to teach the concept.* Empowered Parents. https://empoweredparents.co/sequencing-for-preschoolers/

McLaughlin, M. R. (2011). Speech and language delay in children. *American Family Physician, 83*(10), 1183–1188. https://www.aafp.org/pubs/afp/issues/2011/0515/p1183.html

Megan. (2019, September 13). *Conversation starters for speech therapy - 5 ways to get people talking.* Tactus Therapy. https://tactustherapy.com/conversation-starters-speech-therapy/

Morgenegg, R. (2013, April 27). *Parenting style key for children with developmental disabilities*. Church News. https://www.thechurchnews.com/2013/4/27/23224475/pa renting-style-key-for-children-with-developmental-disabilities

Penn Medicine. (2023). *Speech and language disorders*. Penn Medicine. https://www.pennmedicine.org/for-patients-and-visitors/patient-information/conditions-treated-a-to-z/speech-and-language-disorders#:~:text=A%20speech%20disorder%20is%20a

Prasad, A. H. (2015, April 14). *How do you know when it's a language delay versus a disorder?* Leader Live. https://leader.pubs.asha.org/do/10.1044/language-delay-versus-a-disorder/full/

Presence. (2020, June 28). *The einstein syndrome: Sometimes language delay isn't what you think*. Presence. https://presence.com/insights/the-einstein-syndrome-sometimes-language-delay-isnt-what-you-think/#:~:text=He%20didn

Promoting social-emotional development: The infant and toddler caregiver. (n.d.). VirtualLabSchool. https://www.virtuallabschool.org/infant-toddler/social-and-emotional-development/lesson-5

RCH. (2018, March). *Kids health information : Voice disorders*. RCH. https://www.rch.org.au/kidsinfo/fact_sheets/Voice_disord ers/

Reading Rewards. (2018). *How to start a book club for kids*. Reading Rewards. http://www.reading-rewards.com/blog/how-to-start-kids-book-club/

Rowden, A. (2021, January 6). *Speech therapy: For adults, kids, and how it works*. MedicalNewsToday. https://www.medicalnewstoday.com/articles/speech-therapy#is-it-effective

Savage, L. (2014, September 5). *Negative childhood experiences and health conditions.* The Center for Child Development. https://thecenterforchilddevelopment.com/negative-childhood-experiences-and-health-conditions/

Shrier, C. (2017, October 12). *The importance of talking to your children.* MSU Extension. https://www.canr.msu.edu/news/the_importance_of_talking_to_your_children

Singer, J. (2020). *Play therapy quotes.* Core Wellness. https://www.corewellceu.com/blog/play-therapy-quotes/

SLP, M. (2018, June 8). *Simone says "work on speech and language at home!"* PandaSpeech. https://www.pandaspeechtherapy.com/post/2018/06/08/simone-says-work-on-speech-and-language-at-home

Sowell, T. (2008). *Late-talking children.* Basic Books.

Stallbaumer Rouyer, J., & Davis, P. (2021, September 15). *How to promote diversity and inclusion in your child's life.* ChildrensMercy. https://www.childrensmercy.org/parent-ish/2021/09/diversity/

Tauscher, S. (2019, May 29). *Inspiring quotes on child learning and development.* Vince Gowmon. https://www.vincegowmon.com/inspiring-quotes-on-child-learning-and-development/

Think Kids. (n.d.). *4 causes of speech delays in children.* Think Kids. https://www.thinkkids.com/blog/4-causes-of-speech-delays-in-children

Thought groups and pausing. (n.d.). TFCS. https://tfcs.baruch.cuny.edu/thought-groups/

Trenfor, A. K. (2019, May 29). *Inspiring quotes on child learning and development.* Vince Gowmon.

https://www.vincegowmon.com/inspiring-quotes-on-child-learning-and-development/

Unknown. (2023, May 5). *20 powerful speech therapy quotes*. Number Dyslexia. https://numberdyslexia.com/speech-therapy-quotes/

URMC. (2019). *Language disorders - developmental and behavioral pediatrics*. Rochester. https://www.urmc.rochester.edu/childrens-hospital/developmental-disabilities/conditions/language-disorders.aspx

Velentza, F. (2016, March 5). *Building descriptive skills step-by-step*. Upbility Publications. https://upbility.net/blogs/news/129760071-building-descriptive-skills-step-by-step

Wee Talkers. (n.d.). *Did I cause my toddler's speech delay?* Wee Talkers. https://www.weetalkers.com/blog/did-i-cause-my-toddlers-speech-delay

WHO. (2019, April 24). *To grow up healthy, children need to sit less and play more*. WHO. https://www.who.int/news/item/24-04-2019-to-grow-up-healthy-children-need-to-sit-less-and-play-more

Image References

Danilyuk, P. (2021). Boy in orange shirt playing on the floor [Online Image]. In *Pexels*. https://www.pexels.com/photo/boy-in-orange-shirt-playing-on-the-floor-8422207/

Ethnic girl whispering in ear of friend in living room. (2021). [Online Image]. In *Pexels*. https://www.pexels.com/photo/ethnic-girl-whispering-in-ear-of-friend-in-living-room-7169670/

Holmes, K. (2020). Black woman with pupils in classroom [Online Image]. In *Pexels*. https://www.pexels.com/photo/black-woman-with-pupils-in-classroom-5905557/

Krukau, Y. (2020). A woman sitting on a bed with her son [Online Image]. In *Pexels*. https://www.pexels.com/photo/a-woman-sitting-on-a-bed-with-her-son-6210214/

Krukau, Y. (2021a). A woman teaching kids [Online Image]. In *Pexels*. https://www.pexels.com/photo/a-woman-teaching-kids-8613120/

Krukau, Y. (2021b). Boy in spider man outfit [Online Image]. In *Pexels*. https://www.pexels.com/photo/boy-in-spider-man-outfit-8612893/

Krukau, Y. (2021c). Girl in yellow long sleeve dress reading the alphabets on wall [Online Image]. In *Pexels*. https://www.pexels.com/photo/girl-in-yellow-long-sleeve-dress-reading-the-alphabets-on-wall-8613121/

Nilov, M. (2021). Girls sitting beside a woman in black blazer [Online Image]. In *Pexels*. https://www.pexels.com/photo/girls-sitting-beside-a-woman-in-black-blazer-8923261/

Pou, A. (2021). Man in blue crew neck tshirt reading book [Online Image]. In *Pexels*. https://www.pexels.com/photo/man-in-blue-crew-neck-t-shirt-reading-book-9345612/

Syrikova, T. (2020). Mother and baby using a laptop together [Online Image]. In *Pexels*. https://www.pexels.com/photo/mother-and-baby-using-a-laptop-together-3975659/